HIGHLAND READINGS

BY

D. M. MACKENZIE

AUTHOR'S NOTE.

———

THE majority of the pieces contained in this Book were first published many years ago in *The Glasgow Herald*, and some of them have proved suitable for recitation. The volume is respectfully and affectionately dedicated to all purchasers thereof.

INDEX

PART I

INDEX—continued.

PART II

PART I

MACALLISTER DANCES BEFORE THE KING.

Clansmen, the peats are burning bright,
   Sit round them in a ring,
And I will tell of that great night
   I danced before the King.

For as a dancer in my youth
   So great was my renown,
The King himself invited me
   To visit London Town.

My brand new presentation kilt
   And ornaments I wore,
As with my skian-dhu I rapped
   Upon the Palace door.

9

And soon I heard a lord or duke
  Come running down the stair,
Who to the keyhole put his mouth,
  Demanding who was there.

"Open the door," I sternly cried,
  "As quickly as you can!
Is this the way that you receive
  A Highland gentleman?"

The door was opened; word went round—
  "Macallister is here!"
And at the news the Palace rang
  With one tremendious cheer.

The King was sitting on his throne,
  But down the steps he came;
Immediately the waiting Lord
  Pronounced my magic name.

The lovely ladies of the Court,
  With pearls and jewels decked,
All blushed and trembled as I bowed
  To them with great respect.

Slowly at first, with hands on hips,
  I danced with ease and grace;
Then raised my hands above my head,
  And swifter grew my pace.

At last no human eye could see
  My steps so light and quick,
And from the floor great clouds of dust
  Came rising fast and thick.

The King was greatly moved, and shook
  My hand in friendship true.
" Alas!" he cried, "although a King,
  I cannot dance like you!"

And then the gracious Queen herself
  Came shyly up to me,
She pinned a medal on my breast
  For everyone to see.

Her whisper I shall not forget,
  Nor how her eyes grew dim—
" Ah, where was *you*, Macallister,
  That day I married *him*?"

THE LOVE SONG OF HAMISH MACSCATTAN.

There is a girl lives down by the shore,
Close to the ocean's uproarious roar,
And by that same girl I am setting great store—
    Eliza MacCrimmon MacTavish.
      Eliza MacCrimmon,
      Eliza MacCrimmon,
      Eliza MacCrimmon MacTavish.

She lives just by gathering the wilks on the beach,
And all the wilks strive her basket to reach,
For she has a smile and a welcome for each,
    Has Eliza MacCrimmon MacTavish.
      Eliza MacCrimmon, etc.

Long have I loved her in secret despair:
How could I hope for her beauty so rare?
My heart it is bursting my love to declare
    For Eliza MacCrimmon MacTavish.
      Eliza MacCrimmon, etc.

12

For years my employment was mending the road—
Toiling all day with a gaffer to goad:
The thought of Eliza it lightened my load—
        Eliza MacCrimmon MacTavish.
            Eliza MacCrimmon, etc.

But now I'm in charge of the horse and the cart—
They gave me promotion because I was smart,
And at last I can go to the girl of my heart—
        Eliza MacCrimmon MacTavish.
            Eliza MacCrimmon, etc.

I am taking my horse and my cart, clean and neat,
Far out on the beach my Eliza to meet,
And will cast myself down at the lovely bare feet
        Of Eliza MacCrimmon MacTavish.
            Eliza MacCrimmon, etc.

And then I will say, "Come up here in the cart—
Come up with your creel and for Home we will start;
Give up the wilk business and come to my heart,
        Eliza MacCrimmon MacTavish.
            Eliza MacCrimmon,
            Eliza MacCrimmon,
            Eliza MacCrimmon MacTavish.

THE WIDOW MACDOUGALL.

When I heard that my friend John Macdougall was
  dead,
  I called on his widow, her sorrow to share;
She was making the tea, and she wept as she said,
  " Now, Mister Macpherson, just draw in your chair."

Then I said I would come with my trunk and would
  stay
  To help the poor widow the wolf for to scare,
And I mind at the table how sweet she would say,
  " Now, Mister Macpherson, just draw in your chair."

We spoke of Macdougall, whose spirit was fled,
  Of his death so untimely and virtues so rare,
But Flora would smile through her tears as she said,
  " Now Dougald, my dear, will you draw in your
    chair? "

They was countless, the tears for Macdougall we shed,
  But perhaps it was good that himself was not there,
For sometimes at night when the table was spread
  It was " Dougald, my darling, just draw in your
    chair."

So myself said to Flora, " I'm thinking, my dear,
  We have cried for Macdougall enough and to spare,
Macdougall is dead, but Macpherson is here "—
  And I hung up my hat, and I drew in my chair.

MACRORY NO MORE.

———

For the death of MacRory, my chief, I am mourning—
　MacRory the son of MacRory Ban Vohr,
My cheeks they are streaming with tears that are
　　burning,
　To think that the days of my chieftain are o'er.
In vain shall I long for MacRory's returning—
　With grief for my hero my heart it is sore,
　　　My heart it is sore,
　　　My heart it is sore,
　With grief for my hero my heart it is sore.

The winds they are wailing, the woods they are sighing,
　The streams of the hills sing a dirge as they pour;
The wild birds are sadly his coronach crying,
　The death of MacRory they deeply deplore.
Untimely the chief in the cold ground is lying,
　Alas! we shall look on MacRory no more,
　　　MacRory no more,
　　　MacRory no more,
　Alas! we shall look on MacRory no more.

15

His hand it was strong and his heart is was daring,
　He dressed like his fathers in shield and claymore,
And down from the mountains he often went tearing,
　And homeward the wealth of the Sassenachs bore,
Though great was their power, and loud was their
　　swearing,
　　Their herds and their riches he would not restore,
　　　　He would not restore,
　　　　He would not restore,
　　Their herds and their riches he would not restore.

In sorrow I sit on the rocks by my dwelling,
　And watch the white breakers come rolling to shore,
Sad, sad is the ocean—its bosom is swelling
　As it raises its voice in a heart-broken roar—
MacRory is dead! where he's gone there's no telling—
　Cut off at the age of a hundred and four,
　　　　A hundred and four,
　　　　A hundred and four,
　　Cut off at the age of a hundred and four.

ROBINA.

Just wait and I'll tell you a thing that is droll
That happened to me, John Macdonald from Coll:
One night I was walking—just taking a stroll,
    When who did I meet but Robina.

" And is it yourself, dear Robina? " I cried;
" It is long since I saw you, dear John," she replied,
And then I just started to walk by her side,
    And so I went home with Robina.

But when we arrived at the house where she stayed,
I looked with surprise and my heart was dismayed;
The house was so grand that it made me afraid
    Myself was no match for Robina.

" Robina," I said, in a voice that was sad,
" Do you mind when in Coll we was lassie and lad,
Of the joyful and beautiful days that we had
    At cutting the peats, dear Robina? "

" And do you remember how often we met
When the grass with the dew of the evening was wet?
My heart it is full of those memories yet—
    And have you forgotten, Robina? "

B

" My love, it is strange—it was only to-day
My master was talking of raising my pay,
But still I am poor—Can I take you away
    From this mansion so grand, dear Robina? "

Then Robina she turned to myself with surprise,
And with wonder I saw there was tears in her eyes,
When I heard, in the stillness, a window to rise,
    And a lady called sharply, " Robina ! "

" The mistress is calling," the girl said in fear,
" And I must be saying Good-night to you, dear,
For, John—I am only the laundrymaid here "—
    And into the house ran Robina.

Then I stood and I laughed—I was feeling so glad—
Perhaps people thought 'twas a dram that I had—
But I said to myself, " John Macdonald, my lad,
    Yourself is the man for Robina ! "

In the Island of Coll there was married a pair,
And myself and Robina my sweetheart was there,
And I thought as I looked at the maidens so fair
    That the pick of them all was Robina.

And who was the bridegroom, and who was the bride—
The lassie so lovely that stood by his side?
My secret so joyful no more can I hide—
    The pair was just me and Robina.

KATE.

Little Kate, are you there on the beach
    With your bucket of sand,
With your little brown arms that are bare
    And your spade in your hand?

What a beautiful house you have built!
    You have worked well to-day;
But the tide will come in very soon
    And will wash it away.

See, your father is now on his way
    From his work at the farm,
He is weary, and slowly he walks
    With his coat on his arm.

19

" And is this my own Katie? " he cries,
        When he sees you at play :
To his shoulder he lifts you and says,
        " Little girl, come away ! "

" Am I heavy, dear daddie? " you ask
        With your hand in his hair.
" I was tired, little girl," he replies,
        " Till I put you up there."

And he carries you all the way home,
        And he stands at the door ;
" Here, Jemima," he cries, " is a girl
        I found lost on the shore."

" Bring her in," mother says, with a laugh—
        " She is out far too late ; "
Then she scrubs you, and " John," she declares,
        " This is our little Kate ! "

MACRORY'S FAREWELL.

Listen to me, and I will tell my story:
    I came to Glasgow City from Tiree,
My name is John MacAllister MacRory,
    My height without my boots is six feet three.
        I am a man of ancient Highland race,
        Back for a thousand years my line I trace.

On landing here I made a great impression,
    A job they gave me on the police force,
And in the higher walks of my profession
    I'm noted as a man of much resource.
        And I may say that I have never failed
        To run my man to earth and have him jailed.

Proud have I often been of my vocation,
    Standing at busy crossings in command.
Carters beheld my frown with consternation,
    And trembled at the raising of my hand.
        Yet, in discharging this great public trust,
        No man can say that I have been unjust.

21

But now I have to make an intimation—
　　If you have tears prepare to shed them now—
I've handed to the Chief my resignation;
　　　Great beads of sweat came rolling down his brow.
　　　　On night-shift duty I have been of late,
　　　　And heard at midnight hour the voice of Fate.

For, as I stood and leaned upon a railing,
　　And fondly thought of home in far Tiree,
I heard the wind upon the moorland wailing,
　　　The sound of ocean breakers came to me.
　　　　That night I heard afar the wind and wave,
　　　　While all around was silent as the grave.

And then I thought I heard my mother calling:
　　"Come back to me, my only son," she pled;
And then I saw her face—her tears were falling—
　　　"Your father's growing old and frail," she said.
　　　　And can I stay, as if I did not hear
　　　　The call of Duty and my mother dear?

And so farewell, my friends—your names are legion;
　　Farewell, Lord Provost and Town Council too;
Although departing for a distant region,
　　　Be sure MacRory oft will think of you.
　　　　May Wisdom dwell within your Council Hall,
　　　　And Honour be the star that guides you all.

Perhaps some tourists, knowing not my story,
　　May one day see me in the byre or stye,
And say in wonder—" Is not this MacRory,
　　　Once bulked so largely in the public eye?"
　　　　Yet weep not, friends—no need for sigh or sob!
　　　　I've left the Force—I never liked the job.

"MOHOGGER."

(Mo thogair means " I care nothing.")

His name was Neil—a Highland lad,
In ragged kilt of tartan clad;
A queer by-name the youngster had—
       " Mohogger."

He got it thus : When he was wee
He fell from off his mother's knee,
Yet cried as clearly as could be—
       " Mohogger."

But love to Neil was soon denied—
His father and his mother died,
Yet, being a bairn, the laddie cried—
       " Mohogger."

Ah! sad was now the orphan's way—
He toiled through boyhood's time of play;
Yet, brave and sweet, he'd often say—
       " Mohogger."

The boy became a man, and still
He fought his battle with a will—
His bold reply to every ill—
   " Mohogger."

Love came and knocked upon his door,
And told of happiness in store—
It seemed as if he'd say no more—
   " Mohogger."

But ah! how sad a thing is life!
Neil married with a scolding wife;
His slogan sounded in the strife—
   " Mohogger."

At length one night her spirit fled;
The doctor whispered " She is dead!"
Neil lit his pipe and calmly said—
   " Mohogger."

THE BARD.

———

Among the Highland hills there is a bard
   Whose foot has never left his native glen,
Yet through the Gaelic world his voice is heard
   In songs that stir the hearts of Highland men.

I am the man, and I am pleased and proud
   To state that I am Duncan Macintyre,
The one and only Highland Bard endowed
   With true and genuine poetic fire.

Though I am one that many maids admire,
   From ties of love I always stood apart,
Showing such maidens that my sole desire
   Was to pursue the study of my art.

The daughter of the Chief one night confessed
   That I supreme in her affections reigned,
And while the damsel sobbed upon my breast
   My delicate position I explained.

" Morag," I said, " Alas! it cannot be,
   For while I grant your beauty and your grace
I may not wed—a genius like me
   Belongs not to himself but to his race."

In resignation sweet she bowed her head,
    Although with grief her heart was like to break.
"Duncan, my one and only love," she said,
    "I will remain unmarried for your sake."

"No, no," I said, "that will not do at all,
    There is no sense in giving way to grief,
For there are scores of warriors great and small
    Would gladly wed the daughter of the Chief."

"Never!" she cried, "I scorn that cut-throat crew
    Who think of nought but claymores, knives and dirks
How can I care for anyone but you?
    For I have read your great, immortal works."

I gazed upon her fair and lofty brow,
    I put my arm around her slender waist.
"Morag," I said, "I never knew till now
    You had such splendid literary taste."

I kissed her lovely lips in ecstasy,
    And then, ochone! the fat was in the fire,
For after that there was no choice for me
    But just to make her Mistress Macintyre.

THE BEST DRESSED HIGHLANDER.

(At Highland Gatherings of the past there was commonly a prize for " The Best Dressed Highlander *at his own expense* "— the proviso as to expense being to prevent competitors appearing in borrowed plumes.)

My name is John Macleod—from Chiefs descended
   Distinguished for their courage and their size.
A Highland Gathering lately I attended,
   Because I saw there was to be a prize
      For the best dressed Highlander,
      The best dressed Highlander,
      The best dressed Highlander
         At his own expense.

My kilt and tartan stockings I was wearing,
   My claymore and my dirk and skian-dhu ;
And when I sallied forth with manly bearing
   I heard admiring whispers not a few—
      " He's the best dressed Highlander,
      The best dressed Highlander,
      The best dressed Highlander
         At his own expense."

The ladies, bless them ! came and gathered round me,
   And gazed upon my form so strong and proud.
With ties of gratitude the dear ones bound me,
   When they declared at once that John Macleod
      Was the best dressed Highlander,
      The best dressed Highlander,
      The best dressed Highlander
         At his own expense.

The judge—a man of sense and penetration—
Would go no further when he came to me.
" My choice is clear," he said, " on this occasion,
For John Macleod, as any fool can see,
    Is the best dressed Highlander,
    The best dressed Highlander,
    The best dressed Highlander
        At his own expense."

That night I wrote a letter to my mother
And sent to her the prize that I had won.
She is my faithful love—I have no other—
And proud she'll be that I, her loving son,
    Was the best dressed Highlander,
    The best dressed Highlander,
    The best dressed Highlander
        At his own expense.

The world has many shining paths of glory,
And I have chosen out this path for me—
That John Macleod, until he's old and hoary,
At every Highland gathering will be
    Just the best dressed Highlander,
    The best dressed Highlander,
    The best dressed Highlander
        At his own expense.

THE NIGHT POLICEMAN'S
SERENADE.

Are you awake, Johann, and do you hear me—
　Your own true lover Constable Munro?
O speak to me, my only love, and cheer me,
　Beneath your window walking to and fro.
　　Softly to you I raise my voice in song,
　　And you can hear my footsteps all night long.

For all the night I'm walking—always working,
　I take no rest when I am on my beat,
Save when in some dark doorway I am lurking,
　To peer suspiciously along the street.
　　And when I find there's not a soul in view,
　　I stand awhile, Johann, and dream of you.

O my beloved, just put a shawl about you,
And let me see your face so sweet and fair;
I cannot and I will not live without you,
To be my wife you must at once prepare.
I now emit a declaration true
Of that deep love, Johann, I bear to you.

Are you asleep? I wonder do you hear me—
I hope I am not breaking your repose.
Come to the window, love, and do not fear me,
While I the secret of my heart disclose.
Listen, my love, so beautiful and sweet—
My life is yours—my heart is at your feet.

Or can it be, Johann, that your affection
Is fixed upon some other man than me?
If so, he cannot long escape detection—
Then from the wrath that's coming let him flee.
If there is such a man, let him beware—
My hand is heavy, and I will not spare.

But no! my love, I will not be down-hearted,
I cannot think that you my love despise,
For I depone that last night when we parted
I saw that love was shining in your eyes.
Are you asleep, Johann, or are you dead?
Come to the window and put out your head.

GLASGOW BRIDGE.

When I was sixteen years, my father said—
" Get out of here, you dog, and earn your bread!"
And so I came from Mull to Glasgow Town,
And in an honest job I settled down.

My work was washing bottles in a store,
I'd charge of bottles, big and small, galore;
At first it fairly took my breath away
To see so many emptied every day.

'Twas cold and lonely working underground,
But soon a certain cure for that I found:
When lonely, Gaelic songs I used to sing;
When I was cold, I danced the Highland Fling.

But ah! when evening came I was distressed,
Upon my lonely heart a burden pressed;
In Glasgow City—great, and good, and free—
There was no friendly voice to speak to me!

One evening as on Glasgow Bridge I stood
And watched the flood in melancholy mood,
I heard the music of the pipes draw near—
Strains that to every Highlander are dear.

And then I saw a crowd of maids and men
That hailed from Highland shore and hill and glen,
The marks of toil and battle in their face,
But still a strong, indomitable race.

I knew their stamp of face—my kindly folk!
And oh! I knew the language that they spoke;
I knew and loved them all—to them unknown,
With hungry heart I claimed them all my own.

Then one big fellow, dressed in navy blue,
Said to me, "Donald, when did you come through?
I knew your father—yess, I knew him well,
And many a bar about him I could tell."

Ah me! he saw that I was just a clown,
He seemed to know that I had half a crown;
"I'll pay it back," he said, and went away,
But never have I seen him to this day.

O Glasgow Bridge, you're dear—you're dear to me,
And yet it haunts me still, this memory,
That I, upon your noble granite span,
Lost half a crown and all my faith in man.

THE BAKER.

One day a baker ran to his work
　　At four o'clock in the morning—
His duty he did not intend to shirk
　　At four o'clock in the morning.
But why did he run?　Oh strange to say,
The baker was *late* for his work that day—
Late for his work though he ran all the way—
　　At four o'clock in the morning!

His trade he did not attempt to conceal
　　At four o'clock in the morning,
For his clothes were covered with flour and meal
　　At four o'clock in the morning.
Oh, what a horrible life has he,
Rising perhaps between two and three
In order that he at his baking may be
　　At four o'clock in the morning.

C

The baker rises in winter-time too,
　　At four o'clock in the morning—
A dreadfully difficult thing to do
　　At four o'clock in the morning.
His way through lonely streets he takes
Long hours before the morning breaks,
And he bakes, and bakes, both loaves and cakes,
　　At four o'clock in the morning.

Frequently bakers are killed by the frost
　　At four o'clock in the morning,
And bakers in snowdrifts have often been lost
　　At four o'clock in the morning.
Friend, though your loaf be ever so nice,
Pause, oh pause, at the fourteenth slice,
And pity the wretch who has paid the price
　　At four o'clock in the morning.

THE COMING OF AGE.

A bonfire on the hill is blazing,
  Triumphantly the bagpipes sound,
The clansmen raucous roars are raising
  That echo from the hills around.
    Each heart is glad, from child to sage—
    To-night the Chief has come of age.

Beside the fire an ox is roasting
  And close by is a bowl of salt,
While old and young the Chief are toasting
  In usquebagh of strongest malt.
    Reluctantly we tell the tale,
    Yet truth o'er scruple must prevail.

A score of bards and harpers hoary
  Recall prodigious deeds of old,
Yet oft suspend their song and story
  And leave the lofty tale half told.
    For though the theme be great and high
    The throat of Genius grows dry.

The sennachie proceeds recounting
  The Chieftain's ancient pedigree—
A race that ruled the glen and mountain
  Since human beings came to be.
    So oft has he the tale gone through
    That now himself believes it true.

Full many a man and maid are dancing
With boundless energy and zest,
Around the bonfire they are prancing
For hours on end without a rest.
Thus danced their ancestors of old
To keep themselves from catching cold.

But suddenly the dance is ended,
The songs and laughter die away—
The Chief has now a cask ascended,
His noble form in full array.
The Clan with reverence draws near
The Chieftain's maiden speech to hear.

He stands before them, tall and dashing,
His mighty claymore in his hand,
His martial eyes are fiercely flashing,
As loud he roars the stern command—
"Let every man his thirst assuage
For I the Chief have come of age."

No more he said—and to be truthful
The clansmen all had heard enough
To tell them that their Chieftain youthful
Was made out of the proper stuff.
Here was a man of solid sense—
The Clan would die in his defence.

A HIGHLAND WELCOME.

Did you see in the paper that comes from the North
   That young John Maclean, of Portree,
Was met by his friends in that noble hotel
   That stands in the shore of the sea?

A purse full of sovereigns the lucky John got—
   A token of love and goodwill,
For John was about to depart for the south,
   A job of importance to fill.

" I am sure," said the Chairman, " that with him he
     bears
   The good wishes of everyone here,
And we hope that success will attend our young friend
   When he enters upon his new sphere."

Now I thought that the Skyemen in Glasgow should
     show
   Some regard for the advent of John,
And it might be as well his acquaintance to make
   Before all the sovereigns was gone.

We heard that young Mac was arriving by train,
   And so to the station we went.
" Ochone ! " said poor John, as we parted that night,
   " The first of my sovereigns is spent."

SANDY.

Poor wee Sandy, he wanted to play,
But the bairns on the village green warned him away,
For Sandy was always more ragged than they—
      Fearful wee, tearful wee Sandy!

Poor boy Sandy, alack and alas!
At school he was always the dunce of the class;
That thick-headed laddie no standard could pass—
      Glowering, cowering Sandy!

Poor lad Sandy, he never could learn
Any business by which he a living might earn;
And the world with her weaklings is ruthless and stern—
      Wondering, blundering Sandy!

Poor Sandy, unwanted, superfluous man,
Attempted to shorten life's sorrowful span;
But the law of the land interfered with his plan—
      Reckless man, feckless man Sandy!

Poor old Sandy, he took to his bed,
For he hadn't any fire and he hadn't any bread,
And he laughed to himself when he found he was dead—
      Wicked old, stickit old Sandy!

GENERAL WADE.

There was a man lived long ago,
Whose name all Highlanders should know—
The man I mean is General Wade,
Who roads throughout the Highlands made.
From dawn of day till fall of night
He worked with all his main and might.
Although his task was hard and long,
His heart was brave, his arm was strong.
The Highlanders, so wild and rude,
In crowds around the toiler stood.
Amazed were warrior and bard
To see a man who worked so hard;
Yet heedless of their wondering look,
No notice of the horde he took,
But raised his mighty pick on high
And at the stubborn rocks let fly.

Then with his spade went o'er the ground,
Adjusting every stone and mound,
Nor did he deem the path complete
Until he tramped it with his feet.
And thus it was by skill and strength
The Highland roads were made at length.
Now by these roads the Gaels came down
To earn their bread in London Town,
And there, where riches much abound,
A happy hunting place they found,
And speedily, by hook and crook,
From Englishmen their wealth they took;
And so from Wade's industrious toil
The Gael has reaped a golden spoil.
His bosom therefore surely should
Be filled with lasting gratitude
And kind regard for General Wade,
The hero of the pick and spade.

PRINCE CHARLIE IN GLASGOW.

In seventeen forty-five, that year of grace,
Prince Charlie of the royal Stuart race
Appeared in Glasgow with his Highland host,
And asked to see the Bailies and Provost.

" I want twelve thousand shirts," he sternly said,
" To clothe the men who for their King have bled.
The matter cannot longer brook delay—
Their present shirts are almost worn away."

The Bailies grumbled, but the shirts were brought,
And while to pick the best the warriors fought,
Prince Charlie cleared his throat and spoke again—
" I must have coats and vests for all my men."

To this the Magistrates demurred with heat,
But Charlie said, " My list is not complete—
A bonnet for his head each man must get,
And boots and stockings to keep out the wet."

The Highland army northward took its way,
Dressed in the clothes for which it did not pay,
And all the natives of the Highland fells
Rejoiced to see their relatives such swells.

Upon Culloden Moor there was a fight
When Charlie's well-dressed men were put to flight.
Ah! when the tidings of the battle spread,
Full many a Scottish heart with sorrow bled.

A thousand bards forthwith began to wail
The downfall of the brave and kindly Gael,
But vengeance to the human heart is dear,
And Glasgow did not shed a single tear.

The citizens' delight was unconcealed,
Loudly the city bells in triumph pealed :
The Magistrates of grief made no pretence,
But had a banquet at the town's expense.

THE BELLE OF THE BALL.

On the night when the Chief of the Clan came of age,
   There was dancing and joy in the old castle hall,
And I saw when the dancers was going to engage
   That Kirsty MacCall was the belle of the ball.

She was dressed in a frock that was flowing and long,
   Her step it was light and her waist it was small,
Yet no girl in the hall was so healthy and strong
   As Kirsty MacCall, the belle of the ball.

As for me, I was dressed in my sporran and kilt,
   That showed to advantage my figure so tall,
There was no one so straight nor so splendidly built
   As myself when I danced with the belle of the ball.

We danced in a style that was lively and free,
   Our dancing compelled admiration from all,
And most of the Clansmen was jealous of me
   When they saw how I danced with the belle of
      the ball.

The Chief he arose from the banquet so grand,
    And stood like a king at the head of the hall.
And he said—"I have here a small gift in my hand
    To give to the girl that is belle of the ball."

Then each Clansman spoke up for the girl of his heart
    In the hope that the prize to his sweetheart would fall,
But Kirsty she sat full of sadness apart—
    Her name was not mentioned as belle of the ball.

So I took from my stocking my good skian-dhu,
    And I faced the whole clan with my back to the wall.
And I cried—"Who will dare to deny it is true
    That Kirsty MacCall is the belle of the ball?"

It was well for my foes that the Chief kept his head,
    And by his great power prevented a brawl.
"I will look at the ladies," he graciously said,
    "And myself will decide who is belle of the ball."

He commanded the girls to appear in his sight,
    With judgment and care he inspected them all,
Then he said to myself: "You are perfectly right—
    For Kirsty MacCall is the belle of the ball."

He tenderly kissed her—I watched him with pain—
    For me there is nothing but sorrow and gall;
I sigh and I long for my Kirsty in vain—
    The Chief is away with the belle of the ball.

THE PIPER OF THE CLAN MACRAE.

I am the Piper of the Clan Macrae,
　A clan of doughty deeds and high renown;
There is no bagpipe tune I cannot play,
　On me my father's mantle has come down.

My father was the famous Ronald Rhu,
　For piping he was known both far and wide;
The bagpipes all his life he bravely blew,
　Until at last for want of breath he died.

His pipes upon his manly bosom lay,
　" Take them, my son," he said, and died content.
The teardrops from my eyes I dashed away,
　And for him played a masterly lament.

His wake it was a glorious affair,
　Myself provided the refreshments free;
Each guest made sure that he would get his share,
　And all was happy as a wake could be.

But there was one who sat apart and sighed;
  It was the Chief—that warrior brave and true.
"There is no piper in the world," he cried,
  "Can fill the empty brogues of Ronald Rhu."

My youthful cheek with modesty was flushed,
  As on my father's pipes my hand I laid;
And while the hall in silence deep was hushed,
  The grand old gathering of the clan I played.

Spell-bound they listened as I paced the hall
  With lofty head and proud majestic stride.
The martial fire then stirred within them all,
  And loud the slogan of the clan they cried.

And then I brought them back to earth again
  With strains of grief that thrilled them through and
      through;
They wept aloud, those wild and warlike men,
  While gazing on the corpse of Ronald Rhu.

Not so the Chief—"Enough of this!" he said,
  Addressing with reproof his weeping clan;
"I know quite well that Ronald Rhu is dead,
  But in his place we have *a better man*."

And then his arms around my neck he threw.
  "I never heard," he cried, "such perfect play;
I have much pleasure in appointing you
  To be the Piper of the Clan Macrae."

THE SINGER.

The day that I was born my father proudly
  Acknowledged me and took me on his knee;
My infant cries he drowned by singing loudly
    A Gaelic song to me.

The songs he sang had neither rhyme nor reason,
  His voice got no assistance from his ear;
The noise he made both in and out of season
    Was horrible to hear.

At last, when I upon my manhood entered,
  So full of gall and wormwood was my cup,
To check my parent's bellowing I ventured—
    " Father," I said, " shut up! "

      *   *   *   *   *

I fled afar: the years went swiftly flying,
  Yet never did I see my father's face;
Though often in the city I was sighing
    For my dear native place.

Among the hills my fancy it went soaring,
  I longed to see the scenes of boyhood's days;
But all in vain—my father still was roaring
    His endless Gaelic lays.

But now I hear his singing days are ended,
　　Which makes the hearts of all his friends rejoice;
On him a timely judgment has descended,
　　　　For he has lost his voice.

O joyful news! his vocal powers are vanished,
　　Peace reigns upon the hill and in the glen,
And now the faithful son, unjustly banished,
　　　　Can homewards turn again.

I will arise and go unto my father,
　　A pound of black tobacco in my hand,
And joyfully with him I shall forgather
　　　　In my own native land.

THE HAMMER AND THE BALL.

Sweet Summer, you are here again at last—
   The time of Highland games and sports withal!
Engagements now on me are crowding fast
   To throw the hammer and to put the ball.

These are the grand old sports in which I shine
   And find delight—all other pastimes pall;
All through the winter wearily I pine
   To throw the hammer and to put the ball.

And in these ancient sports supreme I stand,
   To me the prizes and the trophies fall,
For I am powerful and strong of hand
   To throw the hammer and to put the ball.

'Tis strange indeed that two such gifts should be
   Conferred upon one individual,
But who can fathom Providence' decree?
   I throw the hammer and I put the ball.

D

I know a girl that's beautiful and true—
  For years she held my throbbing heart in thrall,
Yet, strange to say! it seems she never knew
  I throw the hammer and I put the ball.

I courted her in vain—till sick and sore,
  My lot in life was bitterness and gall,
And in despair I turned me more and more
  To throw the hammer and to put the ball.

Strange chance! my rival took her to the games
  Where thousands watched me break the records all,
And there she saw that poor rejected James
  Could throw the hammer and could put the ball.

And then I met the girl by chance one night—
  How beautiful she was, and straight and tall!
"Ah me!" I thought, "no more can I delight
  To throw the hammer and to put the ball.

Yet she was gracious, and again I dared
  In desperation at her feet to fall;
"Dear James," she murmured—little then I cared
  About the hammer or about the ball.

And as my arms around her then I threw—
  That scene with joy I tremble to recall!
With radiant eyes she whispered "Only you
  Can throw the hammer or can put the ball."

THE SNOW MAN.

All day in the square where the children played
   He stood in the self-same place,
A great big man with a lofty head
   And a grave and a noble face.

There were two little girls afraid to come near,
   The man seemed so big and so wild;
But soon they were sure that he held them dear,
   And they looked in his face and smiled.

He watched as they played, and it pleased him well
   To see their delight in the snow;
But mother came out when the evening fell
   And said it was time to go.

Say Good-night to the big, brave man, she said,
   For he says he is going to stay
And watch all night while you sleep in bed,
   To keep all the bogeys away.

Two children rose in the dark of the night,
And looked out on the lonely square,
And saw that the man, in the pale moonlight
Was standing and watching there.

A brave, brave man who was not afraid
Of the cold and the eerie night!
Yet the children saw that the moonlight played
On a face that was ghastly white.

And little Annette with the curly head,
She prayed for the man in the snow,
For maybe, she said, he should be in his bed,
But he doesn't know where to go.

When the children rose it was raining hard,
And the snow was away, they found,
And they wept for the man who had stood on guard
For he lay stone-dead on the ground.

The two little girls are big girls now,
And handsome, and bonnie, and bright;
But still they remember the hero, and how
He died at his post that night.

THE PILGRIM.

Far in the North, in olden time,
  There dwelt a famous clan
Whose deeds were known in every land
  Trod by the foot of man.

Descendants of that ancient race
  In every country roam,
And few of them have seen the place
  That was their fathers' home.

For now deserted is the Glen
  Where dwelt the Clan of yore,
Roofless the ancient stronghold stands,
  The fields are tilled no more.

At fall of eve a stranger stood
  Beside those walls so bare,
An aged man whose aspect bore
  The marks of toil and care.

Both old and worn, his garments proved
  That he had known distress,
Yet in his eyes there glowed a fire
  Of strength and nobleness.

Long, long he gazed upon the Glen,
  And, as the moments passed,
He drooped and trembled, and with grief
  His face was overcast.

In mournful tones he cried aloud,
　Though there was none to hear,
" Far have I come to view the land
　Of those whose name I bear.

" Fondly I hoped that kindred here
　Would shake me by the hand,
And kindly bid me welcome home
　To this my fathers' land.

" Alas! no sign of life I see
　Save that of beast and bird,
And 'neath the cairns I see around
　My clansmen lie interred."

With bursting heart the aged man
　Sank down upon the ground,
And night-winds chill, in search of prey,
　His feeble body found.

Lo, as he lay in stillness deep,
　And darker fell the night,
A vision strange appeared, that turned
　His grief into delight.

The darkness passed, and he beheld
　Unto his couch draw nigh
The generations of the Clan
　That lived in days gone by.

A countless host of maids and men,
　The aged and the young,
And in their midst the noble Chief
　Whose deeds the bards have sung.

With ecstasy of joy he knew
    These for his own dear folk;
They clasped the aged Pilgrim's hand,
    And words of welcome spoke.

" Oh faithful son," the Chieftain said,
    " No stranger here art thou,
Behold the kindred thou hast sought,
    Who bid thee welcome now.

" Far hast thou wandered ere at last
    Homeward thy footsteps turned,
Yet ne'er was dimmed the lamp of love
    That in thy bosom burned.

" Oh not in vain thy constancy!
    Thy pilgrimage is o'er,
And by thy kindred shalt thou be
    Beloved for evermore."

His soul had passed; and on his face,
    As on the heath he lay,
There was that peace which nought on earth
    Can give or take away.

THE SOPHIST.

"The uses of adversity
Are sweet," when poor they said to me.
But now that I am rich they say
I ought my wealth to give away.
I cannot tell which way to turn,
Though to do good my heart doth yearn.
For if good to the poor I be,
He knows no more adversity,
Whose uses sweet, so oft extolled,
Him in his poverty consoled.
Shall I, to gain a selfish joy,
The sweetness of his lot destroy?
Nay, nay! for now I clearly see
'Tis best for him and best for me
That I the poor man's cry ignore,
Keep all my wealth and gather more.

THE BAGPIPES.

To Scotland's shore I have come back,
   And I have brought with me
The bagpipes I have often played
   In lands across the sea.

And now I go to end my days
   Back to my native place—
That Highland glen where lived and died
   The people of my race.

And there my bagpipes I will play,
   And all the hills will hear
The splendid music I will make,
   Resounding far and near.

Deep is the love I bear to those
   Great pipers of the past
Whose music cheered my kindred's path,
   Toilsome and overcast.

Imprisoned all the winter through
  By mountains wild and steep,
Each bridle path and mountain track
  In snowdrifts buried deep,

Oh what was then the gift sublime
  That cheered the clansman's heart?
What but the music of the pipes
  When played with skill and art.

When did its magic power fail
  To charm his gloom away,
And make the castle and the cot
  With dance and laughter gay?

In days of lamentation, too,
  The pibroch had its part,
The funeral dirge, proclaiming woe,
  Yet cheered the mourner's heart,

As if a host of loving friends
  Had joined the funeral band,
Singing a noble coronach
  In voices rich and grand.

Throughout the world, in every clime,
  The Gael has wandered far,
And suffered hardship and neglect
  Alike in peace and war.

Yet even in the darkest hour,
  With all his hopes laid low,
The glorious music of the pipes
  Will set his heart aglow.

SPRING-TIME.

The Spring is come; for in the nursery
Wherein I labour daily I can see
Such evidence in every flower and plant,
As any reasonable man can want.
The sunflower, saffron, scabious, and the stock,
Helenium, helianthus, hollyhock,
Begonia, bellis, buttercup, bluebell,
Petunia, poppy, pansy, pimpernel,
Sweetwilliam, starwort, southernwood, sweetpea,
Prunella, primrose, pink and peony,
Carnation, cress, chrysanthemum, catch-fly,
Osmanthus, orchid, orobus, ox-eye,
Pentstemon, privet, pelargonium,
Marjoram, mint, mesembryanthemum—
All these and many others I could name,
The presence of the glorious Spring proclaim.
Then in the humble vegetable world
The cabbage leaf is quietly unfurled,
The carrot, onion, leek, and Brussels sprout
Declare that Spring is here without a doubt.
If any man on further proof insist
I may refer him to our nursery list
Of flowers and plants (the cheapest and the best)
Which will be sent post free upon request.

THE POLICEMAN AT THE SCHOOL.

At the request of special friends,
  I am about to try
To tell you all about myself—
  Angus Macleod from Skye.

Some years ago myself arrived,
  Straight from the Misty Isle,
To see if I could find a job
  That would be worth my while.

And, oh! for many a weary day
  I walked and walked the street,
Home-sickness in my Highland heart
  And blisters on my feet.

The Polis Force suspected that
  I was on mischief bent,
And one night they arrested me
  For loitering with intent.

They took me to their Chief—a man
    Much feared by low and high,
But I was not afraid—I knew
    That he was born in Skye.

His beard was white as driven snow,
    His nose was red as fire,
His eyes was blue, and from their depths
    There blazed perpetual ire.

" Now, glacker mhor," he sternly asked,
    " What wass you doing here? "
" Just looking for a job," I said,
    In Gaelic accents clear.

" Ah, bronain bhochd," he said to me,
    " And ciamar ha shein dieu?
You speak the Gaelic—and myself
    Will give a job to you."

Upon the Polis Force my name
    Was then at once put down,
Where thousands of the men of Skye
    Won glory and renown.

Myself indeed began to dream
    Of glory more and more;
I dreamed of catching countless thieves
    And burglars by the score.

And if there was a murderer
    That no one else could trace,
Myself would track the scoundrel down
    And charge him to his face.

Then criminals of every class,
　　Whenever I drew near,
Would turn as pale as ghosts and fly
　　To hide themselves in fear.

Ochone! the truth I must confess—
　　Pride went before my fall;
The Chief one day declared I was
　　No use at all, at all.

" There is a public school," he said,
　　" That now will be your beat;
All you are fit for is to help
　　The bairns across the street."

In vain—in vain was all my dreams,
　　My name unknown to fame;
And when I started at the school
　　I nearly died with shame.

Yet by-and-bye, as I began
　　To know the bairns by sight,
I got to like the truaghans,
　　So innocent and bright.

And now, no more I am ashamed,
　　For lately I have grown
As fond of all the boys and girls
　　As if they was my own.

And what is more—and strange indeed
　　As it may seem to be—
Although I am a Polisman,
　　The bairns is fond of me.

CALUM VOYACH.

There was a chap once lived on earth,
A man of music and of mirth,
Who from his very hour of birth
    Was known as Calum Voyach.

He dwelt the Highland hills among—
A lonely man, no longer young;
No language but the Gaelic tongue
    Was known to Calum Voyach.

His little house was poor and bare,
And miles and miles from everywhere,
Yet dancers old and young went there
    To learn from Calum Voyach.

No man among the Highland hills
Could play the Lancers or Quadrilles,
Or rouse the Reel of Tulloch thrills,
    So well as Calum Voyach.

At every marriage in the land
His services were in demand,
For at the dance the total band
    Was fiddling Calum Voyach.

Of all the people gathered there
To grace the bridal of the pair,
The man most gay and debonair
    Was always Calum Voyach.

To millions in the world to be,
Where harps resound eternally,
A welcome interlude would be
    A dance by Calum Voyach.

TOM.

There was a man whose name was Tom;
Nobody knew where he came from,
Nor was it known where he went to,
Or what he did, or was to do.

Where did he stay?   He could not say,
And never was there anyway;
So if the man was never there
His home might be just anywhere.

His parents' home he did not know,
To call on them he could not go;
To call on folk is foolishness
Unless you know their right address.

No pride of race, or family tree,
Or famous ancestors had he;
An ancestor that no one knows,
Seldom, if ever, famous grows.

Directories Tom scanned, no doubt,
His name and dwelling to find out,
But he was handicapped because
The fellow knew not who he was.

Abandoned, derelict, unknown,
In exile wandering alone,
By half the world remembered not,
And by the other half forgot.

Oh why should one be doomed by Fate
To be thus lost and desolate?
Such questions cannot answered be,
Shrouded they are in mystery.

One moral from this thoughtful rhyme
Each one should learn and heed in time—
To get and bear your whole life through
Your birth certificate with you.

If Tom that document had worn,
And someone asked where he was born,
Tom surely would not hesitate
To whip out his certificate.

Oh brethren, let us thankful be
For knowing our identity,
In case our uncle, old and wise,
Should leave us money when he dies.

For think how dreadful it would be
If you were left a legacy,
And all your life you never knew
The legacy was meant for you.

Ten thousand pounds the sum might be,
And you engulfed in poverty;
You died—and never got your grip
On any of that cash or scrip.

Oh ghastly thought! oh hideous fate!
Too horrible to contemplate.
From Tom and his concerns we fly,
And gladly bid the wretch Good-bye.

THE ECHO.

A merry lad one evening stood
Among the trees deep in a wood,
The noble trees he loved, and so
He hailed them with a loud Hullo!

And in a moment, strange to say,
Out of the wood, from far away,
Three voices to his call replied—
Hullo, hullo, hullo! they cried.

The little fellow, in delight,
Kept up the game with all his might,
For surely this was glorious fun—
Three calls in answer to his one.

So long and often did he shout,
He could not cut the habit out,
And into manhood did he grow,
Still hailing everyone Hullo!

And lo! the rule remains the same
As when of old he played the game—
His call of cheer to fellow men
Returns three-fold to him again.

PART II

FINGAL'S CAVE.

NIGHT came down on Staffa Isle. Fingal sat in his cave before a peat fire, at which his daughter, the white-bosomed, red-armed Flora, was toasting bannocks. A kilted gillie held a bossy shield above Fingal's head to prevent the water that dripped from the roof going down the King's neck. In a corner a number of warriors lay asleep on beds of heather, and throughout the cave Ossian and fifteen other bards sat on heaps of broken stalactites, raising their voices in song and twanging their harps in harmony. But such was the noise of the waves as they came rolling far into the cave that Fingal the King heard not the voices of the bards as they sang the glorious tale of his victories.

A watchman drew near and roared into Fingal's ear that a party of strangers were at the mouth of the cave and desired to enter.

" Well," yelled Fingal, " you know the usual charge. They are very late. It iss too dark to see the cave now, but the price iss sixpence a head—not a penny less."

The strangers' boat was now rowed into the cave, and its occupants, who seemed much exhausted, were helped on to the dry part of the floor. Fingal was looking earnestly at their leader.

"King Haco of Norway!" he shouted in surprise. "Man, I did not know you—I chust took you for some tourists. How did you get on at Largs?"

Haco shook his head dejectedly. "We could have have made short work of the Scottish army," he bellowed, "but unfortunately for us the battle took place on the Glasgow Autumn Holiday, and Largs was full of Glasgow people. They stoned us out of the place."

On hearing this the bards wanted to console Haco by singing a lament, but Fingal would not allow this. He saw that what Haco and his men needed was food and rest, and so, after a substantial meal of usquebaugh and bannocks, the Norsemen retired for the night.

In the morning, when about to resume his voyage, Haco took Fingal aside and asked him was it really necessary that he should stay in such a noisy, moist, and unhealthy place as the cave. "Come with me," said Haco, "and I will make you Governor of Orkney —no less."

Fingal smiled and shook his head. "A king does not willingly become a vassal," he answered. "But I will tell the whole truth. I stay in the cave only in the warm weather, when I make a good deal off the tourists in the way of admission money and by selling refreshments. And as for the cave being noisy, that iss the chief reason for my staying in it."

" Now, now!—you are pulling my leg," said Haco. " Do you mean to say that you enjoy living in a noise like this? "

" Hush! it iss those bards," said Fingal confidentially. " I could never stand them all the year round at all, at all. You know that I have done a thing or two as a warrior, and the bards are never done singing about me and what I have done. A little of that kind of thing iss very good, but they do not know when to stop, and yet I must not be discouraging them. There iss Ossian, for instance—a decent man, and a clever man, but—" Fingal tapped his forehead meaningly.

" Ay, ay! Do you tell me that?" said Haco.

" Too true!" answered Fingal, with a sigh. " They are all daft. But in the cave, you see, I cannot hear their recitations of poetry and their harp-playing owing to the noise of the sea, and that iss why I am staying there."

" Oh, very good—very ingenious!" cried Haco, breaking into a hearty laugh, in which he was loudly joined by Fingal.

" Ingenious!—that iss what I am thinking myself," said Fingal, looking with great kindness at his guest. " Come now," he added, " and yourself and myself will chust be having a small deoch-an-doruis before you go."

FINGAL'S FIRST-FOOT.

I⊤ is a fact well known to all antiquaries worth mentioning that Fingal, the warrior King of Morven, always made a point of bringing in the New Year at his cave in the Isle of Staffa. One New Year's Eve, as midnight was drawing near, the King sat at the fire in his cave along with his bards and principal warriors, eagerly watching the horologe that would signal the dawn of another year. The tide was out at the time, and the cave was comparatively quiet save for the voices of a group of minor bards, who sat apart and recited their own poetry to each other. On the stroke of twelve Fingal rose from the cask on which he had been sitting.

" Warriors and bards," he cried in his loud, hearty voice, " A happy New Year to everyone of you ! "

This sentiment was at once reciprocated, a deafening roar of good wishes coming from three-score of throats.

The warriors then seized the cask on which the King had been sitting and proceeded hastily to open it.

The high-born and gifted Ossian now poised himself on a large stone and began reciting an ode to the New Year specially composed for the occasion, but to his mortification and the ill-concealed joy of his brother bards his performance was interrupted by a loud altercation at the mouth of the cave.

" My boat wass first, and there iss an end of it," roared a voice of terrific power, and presently a young giant, rivalling Fingal himself in stature, came wading into the cave, carrying two large stone jars, one in each hand.

" Cuthullin, my hero! " cried Fingal, tears of joy starting to his eyes. " And you have come all the way from Skye to first-foot me, my tear poy. And what have you in the jars? "

Cuthullin also was weeping with joy. " It iss chust a drop of Sligachan," he answered brokenly.

" Ha, ha! there iss nothing better," said Fingal with satisfaction, drying his eyes. " But what little priest iss this? "

" I am the new Abbot of Iona," answered a short but dignified man who had followed Cuthullin into the cave.

" He iss the man that wanted to be before me," said Cuthullin indignantly.

" And so you came to first-foot me," said Fingal, looking kindly at the Abbot. " But where iss your gift to me? " he added. " You know that you would bring me bad luck if you wass my first-foot without some present in your hand—no matter how small."

" That is only a superstition," answered the Abbot scornfully.

" Peace," said Fingal. " There iss nothing surer than that you would have brought bad luck to me, but Cuthullin wass too quick for you. Now you will chust join with us in bringing in the New Year. Ossian, strike up a tune."

The Abbot put his fingers in his ears. " I cannot stay here," he cried. " I never taste wine or spirits— I am a teetotaler. And as for your songs—they are the works of the Evil One himself."

A howl of rage came from the bards, while the warriors gazed at the Abbot in astonishment and incredulity. But Fingal had other and kinder thoughts; he took a large Scotch bun wrapped in silver paper from the table and gave it to the Abbot.

" You will take this from me," he said kindly, " it iss chust a little bit of a cake from Glasgow."

" He wass surely joking; what did he call himself? " asked Cuthullin when the Abbot had gone.

" A teetotaler," said Fingal. " My father once told me there wass a strange man like that came to Mull. He chust lived for two or three weeks, and then the rheumatics took him away. But come," he added briskly, " we are wasting time; this iss no way to take in the New Year. Ossian, my poy, come on with your chorus. And Cuthullin, my hero, what will you be having yourself? "

HOMAGE.

AFTER the battle of Largs King Haco of Norway proceeded up the West Coast of Scotland on his way to the Orkneys. On approaching Skye the Norse army was once more in good spirits.

" I suppose," said Haco to the Jarl of Scalpa, " Alexander of Scotland will now expect to come into possession of all the Hebrides. But I will not give up Skye. We will land at Portree and I will receive the homage of the Lord of the Isles."

As the Norse army disembarked at Portree the mist was so thick that no man could recognise his neighbour.

" Does anyone know the way to the hotel? " roared Haco.

After a vain search of some hours the Norsemen suddenly heard the loud swell of the bagpipes, and, guided by the sound, they presently found themselves at the hotel door. Prompted by curiosity, Haco went into the bar, and the first man he saw was Angus Og, Lord of the Isles, himself.

" Angus Og," cried Haco, " I have come to receive your homage."

" Prut, trut! hear to him! " said Angus, turning to a group of chiefs in his company. " There iss no time to-day for homage."

" What! " said Haco, angrily.

" Do you not know that this iss the day of the Portree Games? " Angus asked. " The best thing you can do iss to come with us and see them. But, first, you will choin us in a dram."

Haco coughed, and tapped himself on the chest. "This mist is very wetting," he said in a mollified tone. "Well, well, I will just send my army back to the ships, and I will come with you."

The games were soon in full swing. From the playing of bagpipes, the thumping of feet, and the frequent cries of "Hooch!" Haco gathered that dancing competitions were going forward, but the mist was so dense that he could see nothing of them. After about six hours had passed the water coursing down his body began to tell on him.

"I wish to goodness the games were over," he said. "What is the use of standing here all day when we cannot see anything?"

"These annual games have been held from time immemorial, but they have never been seen, owing to the mist," answered Angus Og in a serious tone. "But although we cannot see them we know that they are going on."

At this moment the result of a jumping competition was announced. "Lachlan Ruadh has won the high chump—fifteen feet nine inches," roared the herald.

"Not a bad chump—not bad, not bad!" said Angus critically.

Haco was marking time with his feet to warm them, when suddenly a large, heavy object went hurtling past his head.

"Great Thor!" he exclaimed, "what was that?"

"They are throwing the hammer," said Angus.

"Well, I am going back to the hotel," said Haco with decision. "I don't see any fun in this."

" Quietly, then, and I will be coming with you," whispered Angus. " It would be a nasty thing if they wass to find that I wass not at the games, but I will risk it all the same."

When they reached the hotel and had warmed themselves at the bar the Lord of the Isles pressed Haco to stay to the dance. " I will lend you a dry kilt," he said, " and I will introduce you to some of the finest girls—you never saw the like of them."

It was five in the morning when Haco arrived on board his flagship and went to bed. By-and-bye he was roused by the Jarl of Scalpa, who was anxious for news.

" Did you receive the homage of Angus Og? " inquired the Jarl.

" Homage ! " exclaimed the King, scratching his head. " Yes, there was homage, but it was myself that paid the homage."

" Homage to Angus Og ! " cried the horrified Jarl.

" No, no—not to Angus Og, you fool," answered the King, " but to the girls, man—the fine, and the lovely, and the beautiful girls of Skye."

GOLF IN MORVEN.

The dominions of Fingal, King of Morven, were once invaded by a Scandinavian monarch named Starno, and after war had been raging for several weeks Starno proposed there should be a truce on the spring holiday, which was drawing near, as some of his men were anxious to have a game of golf. The truce was heartily agreed to by Fingal, and in the forenoon of the holiday he went down to the golf course, accompanied by Cuthullin, the famous warrior of Skye. On arriving at the clubhouse the pair were disgusted to find a large crowd waiting their turn to play off, including all the Scandinavians, who, being visitors, were accorded priority of place in accordance with the romantic courtesy prescribed and practised by Fingal.

"Well, well, it cannot be helped," said Fingal. "The only thing we can do iss to wait in the clubhouse and have a dram."

This suggestion being accepted with resignation by Cuthullin, the two warriors sat at the window and watched the players driving off from the first tee. Fingal described to his friend a new golf ball he had invented. On its core of wood there was a thick layer of dulse or seaweed, and this was firmly secured by an outside covering of white moleskin. Cuthullin began to discuss the points of the invention, when the caddie-master came and informed the two friends that Starno intended breaking the truce and murdering Fingal and all his men.

" Indeed, I wass chust thinking there wass some jookery-pookery about it," said Fingal, knitting his brows. " Ten couples hass left the tee, and of course all of them wass Starno's men. You see the fine chance that he will have."

" What sort of chance? " inquired Cuthullin.

" Treachery! " said Fingal. " Do you not see that Starno's men will all be feenished and be waiting here when we begin to come in—two at a time. They would have us at their mercy."

" Ah! the dirty rascal! but I never wass trusting him," said Cuthullin, spitting on the floor contemptuously. " What will you be going to do? "

" My friend," replied Fingal, " you will go out and you will tell my men secretly that there will be no golf for them to-day. They will stay where they are till Starno's men are all away, and then they will come in here and have a good meal at the public expense."

Fingal then turned to the caddie-master. " How many caddies have you? " he inquired.

" I cannot count them, they are so many," replied the caddie-master.

" Poor poys! " said Fingal softly. " Tell them to scatter themselves over the course and pick up as many as possible of the balls that Starno's men are playing. They must keep well out of sight, but I know I can trust them for that. I am grieved to employ them in this way; but they will enchoy the work, and it will help to fit them for their future course in life."

When the last of Starno's men had played off Fingal's warriors came in and sat down to the best meal the club could provide. After the repast many speeches were made, and Gaelic songs were rendered at intervals. At last Ossian, the head bard, or Poet Laureate, intimated that he had on the spur of the moment composed a song commemorating the occasion, upon which the meeting broke up.

In the dusk of the evening King Starno, followed by his men, entered the clubhouse. His appearance was wild and haggard, and he was greatly agitated.

" The whole day has been wasted looking for balls," he roared hoarsely. " I have lost five balls, and split-new ones at that. Bring me a big glass of whisky instantly."

" Sorry, chentlemen," said the clubmaster, " Fingal and his men hass been here all the day—all the day, chentlemen,—and there is not a trop of trink in the place."

THE WHITE WAISTCOAT.

ONE Glasgow Fair Saturday morning I purchased a third-class ticket and took my place in a first-class compartment of the five-thirty a.m. train for Mallaig. Presently a railway official opened the door and ushered in three young men. Two of them appeared to be of the humbler class, but the other one had on a white waistcoat.

"Yourself iss the poy, Chames—getting us into a first-class," said one of the three, Allister by name, addressing him of the white waistcoat. "Did you give a tip to the guard?"

"No fear!" said James.

"It wass the white waistcoat that did it," said the third man, whose name was Duncan.

"Stand at the window and show your waistcoat, Chames," said Allister, "or else we will be having a lot of common third-class passengers coming in here. And wait now—I have a cigar that you will smoke, and you will put your head out of the window."

81

F

"I hope it iss a cood cigar," said James, suspiciously.
"There iss cigars and cigars."

Late-comers were hurrying up and down looking for seats. Some of them paused and looked daringly at our compartment, but the white waistcoat and cigar were too much for their courage, and they hurried away.

The train started. "Man, Chames," said Allister, "with that waistcoat you look as if you wass making your three pounds a week with the best of them."

"That iss so," put in Duncan. "And you and me, Allister, will have no chance among the girls at all—they will not look at us."

James relit the cigar and puffed at it with an air of criticism. "Be quiet, boys," he said. "I know what iss wrong with you—it iss chust chealousy, because none of you hass got a white waistcoat, and although you had one you would not have the pluck to put it on. Besides, you are too thin; it takes a cood stout man like myself to do chustice to a white waistcoat."

We played halfpenny nap till we reached Fort-William, and here the white waistcoat did noble service again. We wanted to get some refreshment, but around the counter there was a crowd standing four deep. I cannot pretend that these men stood aside to make room for James; in such cases it is every man for himself, and even a white waistcoat is of no avail. But James pressed forward, and when the waitress caught sight of his waistcoat he was served instantly over the head of a little stout Gael right in front. This man cursed heartily in his native tongue, but James only smiled. " That iss a man," he said " that hass no respect for wealth and position. He will be a Socialist."

On approaching Mallaig we acknowledged to James our indebtedness to his white waistcoat, and agreed that it was only fair we should " stand our hands " to him when we got on to the boat. James did not demur. " But I must be taking it off now," he said. " I will not get a chance on the boat."

" Aha! You are chust a coward after all," cried Duncan. " You are afraid to go home in the waist-coat. Poof! poof! "

" Fuich! fuich!" said Allister. " What a come-down! "

" What are you talking about? " said James impatiently, as he changed the white waistcoat for a dark one. " This waistcoat iss chust for travelling, so that I will be respected on the chourney. I cannot afford to wear it at home, for the crofters would be saying, ' Chames is getting on—he iss making his fortune,' and every time I showed my face at the hotel every man of them would be at my heels waiting till I would say, ' What will you be having? ' I have chust three pounds in my pocket, and that will need to do me for a fortnight. But if I went about with my white waist-coat, do you think I could manage with three pounds? I tell you no—it iss not three pounds a day that would see me through."

A GENEALOGICAL INQUIRY.

I became acquainted with Macmillan at a small golfing resort in the Highlands. We met for the first time on the links, and each being without a partner, we went off together. Notwithstanding his Scotch name, he was an Englishman, and during the round, consequently, he supplied me with many particulars about his business and private life.

It turned out that Macmillan and I were staying at the same hotel. That night, about eleven o'clock, he invited me up to his bedroom to have a talk; it seems he was anxious to impart to me any circumstances regarding himself and his family he might have omitted to mention on the golf course.

"I don't mind telling you," he began, " that in business I have done pretty well—my father did well, and I have done better. But success in business it not everything. In England I mix with some rather well-connected people, and I should like very much to be able to say that I am descended from a Highland chief. This has become quite an ambition with me, and I have come here with the object of getting information about my ancestors. The earliest one I know of lived in this town."

Macmillan relit his pipe and looked at me expectantly.

"In this town," I repeated, to show I was gripping the facts.

"Yes," he went on, with that wonderful conversational energy which distinguishes so many Englishmen,

" we have his name in an old Bible at home—Donald Macmillan, born 1712. That is all we know of him."

" I know the registrar here," I said. " He may be able to help you."

Next day we visited the registrar, and found that Donald Macmillan, born 1712, had died in 1750. Curiously enough, however, the register contained no information as to his occupation and place of residence.

We then called on the town bookseller, who had some reputation as a local historian. " Donald Macmillan," he said promptly. " Of course. That is the man— but why do you ask? " he inquired suddenly.

" This is Mr. Macmillan, from London," I said. " Donald Macmillan was his ancestor, and he is anxious to trace——"

The bookseller naturally had a book in his hand, but at this moment it dropped to the floor, and he took a long time to find it behind the counter. When at last he rose his face was very red, and he was coughing violently.

" Yes," he said, " John Macmillan was the man's name, you say? "

" No; his name was Donald."

" Ah—a different man. John was the name of the man I know about."

That very evening, however, the problem was solved. Macmillan and I were sitting along with the Town Clerk on the top of a small hill in the public park. The Town Clerk was talking. " This hill," he said, " is called the Gallows Hill—in the old days they used to hang people here. At that time theft was punishable by death, and hangings were much more common than now. As a matter of fact, that old law was not repealed till quite recently, but it was never enforced here since 1750, when a man was hanged for sheep-stealing.''

'' 1750 ! '' I exclaimed, without thinking.

'' Sheep-stealing ! What was his name? '' Macmillan asked in a hoarse voice.

'' Why,'' said the Town Clerk with a laugh, '' he was a clansman of your own; your asking his name is rather a coincidence. For his name was exactly the same as your own, Donald Macmillan—a born thief and a thorough scoundrel.''

MACKINNON'S KILT.

THE other night I called on Mackinnon to see if he could go with me to the Cowal Games at Dunoon. Mackinnon is a fine figure in the kilt, and at a Highland gathering I am always proud to be in his company.

" No, I cannot be there," he said. " I am terribly sorry to miss the games, but business iss business."

At this moment there was a ring at the door bell, and another member of the Mackinnon clan was shown into the room.

" I am clad to see you, Tuncan," said Mackinnon. " It iss a while since I saw you."

" I wass chust wondering if you wass going to the Cowal Games," said Duncan.

" Nothing would please me better," said Mackinnon " but I cannot go—business iss business."

" Then maybe you would have no obchection to lend me your kilt," said Duncan.

" Man, you are too late," Mackinnon answered. " I have chust promised my kilt to my friend here."

I gave a startled look at Mackinnon, but something in his eye kept me silent. Duncan seemed much disappointed at not getting the kilt, and shortly afterwards took his leave.

" What did you mean by saying that? " I demanded.

" That iss a man," said Mackinnon, " that has often

and often borrowed my kilt, but I am resolved not to give it to him any more. If he iss so fond of the kilt, why will he not buy one for himself? "

" A good kilt is expensive," I said.

" It iss a strange thing this borrowing of kilts," Mackinnon went on. " What would you think of a man that wass always borrowing your dress suit from you, or your frock coat? You would not think much of him. Yet my kilt iss my dress suit. Whenever I want to dress myself in my best, and feel my best, I put on my kilt— it iss the only cood dress that I have cot."

" I suppose people regard it as a fancy dress," I said.

" A fancy dress!—yes, I suppose they do," said Mackinnon angrily. " But it iss not a fancy dress; it iss the everyday dress of some of the finest chentlemen in the land. Oh, I am keen to encourage the wearing of the kilt. When a man will wear the kilt he will learn to walk like a man, and he will take a proper pride in his body and in his looks."

" Well, Mackinnon, I believe you have the right end of the stick," I said as I rose to go.

" I will send the kilt to you in time for the gathering," said Mackinnon.

" But I thought you objected to lending your kilt? "

" You are wrong," Mackinnon replied. " I would not lend it to Tuncan because I am hoping he will buy one for himself. I am anxious that everyone that likes a kilt will buy a kilt—and who knews but you will take a fancy for one yourself? But it always goes to my heart if my kilt iss lying idle when there iss a gathering. Every kilt in Scotland should be at every gathering, and the day will come all the sooner when in the whole of Scotland there will be nothing worn but the kilt."

"I am really obliged to you," I said. "But I'm afraid I should feel queer—I never wore a kilt in my life. My legs——"

"Come, come, be off with you!" said Mackinnon impatiently. "I will give you a pair of extra thick stockings, and your legs, poor as they are, will never be noticed. The man that wears the Mackinnon tartan will be welcomed and honoured wherever he goes."

A HIGHLAND GRAVEYARD.

EVER since the night when the Pedlar was robbed of his money in a lodging-house he has made a habit of sleeping in graveyards, for there he is never molested save by the ghosts. At first he was somewhat afraid of the ghosts, but soon he got used to them. One night he had just laid himself down behind a graveyard wall when a ghost came and leaned against a tombstone and began talking to him.

" My name iss Macdonald—Donald Macdonald," began the Ghost, " and my ancestor wass chief of his clan."

" No doubt—no doubt," said the Pedlar.

" He wass really," said the Ghost. " The Clan Macdonald iss the most ancient, numerous, and powerful in the Highlands, and, as I said, I am directly descended——"

" Highland pride—Highland pride," muttered the Pedlar.

" What wass you saying? " enquired the Ghost.

" Nothing," answered the Pedlar.

" My grandmother's brother went abroad and distinguished himself in the Cherman wars," continued the Ghost.

" Rose to be a sergeant," suggested the Pedlar.

" A cheneral? " said the Ghost impressively. " In birth I am superior to anything in this graveyard—everyone admits it except a fellow called Campbell."

" The Campbells and Macdonalds were always quarrelling," said the Pedlar.

" He hass a grudge against me," went on the Ghost, " because my great-grandfather killed his great-grandfather in battle."

" That iss a lie! " cried a second Ghost, suddenly starting up from behind a tombstone.

" Now, now! " said the Pedlar pacifically.

" It iss chust like him," said the Macdonald ghost, " to come sneaking about and listening to everything I say."

" I suppose this is the Campbell you were speaking of? " asked the Pedlar.

" Yes, I am Campbell—Archibald Campbell," said the second ghost. " My great-grandfather wass chief of the great Clan Campbell."

" No doubt—no doubt! " said the Pedlar.

A curious nasal sneer came from the Macdonald ghost.

" I heard Macdonald say," went on the Campbell ghost, " that his great-grandfather killed my great-grandfather."

" He did—with one stroke of his good claymore," said the Macdonald ghost, smacking his lips.

" Good—good! " murmured the Pedlar.

" As a matter of fact," said Campbell, thrusting forward his head," my great-grandfather killed his great-grandfather."

" What! " roared Macdonald.

" Cut his head off," said Campbell with a savage grin, " and sent it home to your great-grandmother."

A strange dreadful cry came from the Macdonald ghost, and he flew through the air at Campbell. " Take that ! " he yelled.

" Would you—would you?" cried Campbell gallantly. " Come on—come on ! "

The Pedlar sat up and watched the combat. For a while Macdonald pursued Campbell, then Campbell pursued Macdonald.

" Queer—queer ! " murmured the Pedlar, as he lay down to sleep.

But soon the ghosts were back again.

" I have convinced Campbell at last," said Macdonald triumphantly.

" Nothing of the sort ! " cried Campbell. " My great-grandfather——"

" Come, come ! " protested the Pedlar drowsily. " I can't allow this noise. You are keeping the whole graveyard awake."

" Well, Macdonald's story iss chust a fabrication," said Campbell. " You will not believe him, will you ? "

" I don't believe him," the Pedlar answered.

" That's right," said Campbell gratefully.

" Any more than I believe you," said the Pedlar, his eyes closing in slumber.

THE ANONYMOUS DONOR.

ONE night Willie the Pedlar lay down on a recently-made grave in a Ross-shire cemetery. He would have preferred an older grave, but selected this one because it had a large head-stone that protected him from the cold wind. Presently a ghost approached the Pedlar and demanded sternly what he was doing there.

" I'm going to sleep here," replied Willie. " This is not your grave anyway."

" No ; but it belongs to an old friend of mine. Ever since he was buried I have been wanting to speak to him, but he always avoids me."

" This is the Provost's grave," said the Pedlar.

" Yes, it's him I mean. He avoids me so plainly that I have now a strong suspicion he has not been honest with me. I am McCulloch the draper, that was killed in a railway accident about ten years ago. Did you ever hear that I gave five hundred pounds towards the building of the Town Hall? "

" Never heard of it," said the Pedlar. " The only man who gave five hundred pounds was the man that is buried here—Munro, the banker—and he was made Provost on the strength of it."

" My suspicions are then confirmed," said the Ghost, striking his breast tragically. " Let me tell you that the man in that grave—Munro the Provost—is a cheat and a swindler. I gave five hundred pounds to the Town Hall fund, and he took the credit of giving it."

" How did he manage that? "

" You remember I was a Town Councillor," said McCulloch, " and when the old Provost died I stood for the Provostship. There were others keen to get the job, so I determined to make sure of it by giving five hundred pounds to the hall fund. Munro was my banker, and he paid over the money, keeping my name a secret. He also was a Councillor, and I arranged with him that he would let out the name of the anonymous donor at the meeting at which the Provost was to be elected. About a week before the meeting I had to go south on business, and on my way back I was killed in the railway smash."

" All this sounds quite likely," said the Pedlar. " Munro, the banker, was not a candidate for the Provostship till after you were killed; and at the meeting he intimated it was himself that gave the money."

" The scoundrel—not a word about me ! " exclaimed McCulloch passionately. " Come out Munro, if you are a man—come out and defend your character."

In answer to this loud summons the ghost of the Provost slowly emerged from his grave. " I have heard your charge, James," he said. " It is true I did not wish to meet you—I feared you would not believe my side of the story. But now that Willie the Pedlar is here he will corroborate what I say."

" Maybe—maybe," said the Pedlar.

" When you got killed, James," the Provost continued, " nobody was more sorry than I. At first I thought of stating at once that you were the anonymous donor; but things had altered somewhat in the Council during your absence, and the race for the Provostship was now between you and Tom Scott."

" Tom Scott—the low upstart! "

"Exactly. I knew you were at daggers with him, and judged I should best show respect for your memory by using your money to keep him out of the Provostship. The only way to do that was to take the job myself."

" I would have spent my last penny to baulk Tom Scott," said McCulloch, with decision. " If what you say is true, Duncan, you have faithfully interpreted my wishes."

" It is quite true," said the Pedlar.

" I apologise, then, Duncan," said McCulloch with emotion. " Come over to my grave, my old and dear friend, and we will have a fine crack about old times."

THE MURDERER.

At the close of a wet day Willie the Pedlar climbed over the rough stone wall of an ancient Highland grave-yard to look for a bed among the tombs. The grass was long and saturated with rain, and failing to discover a more comfortable couch, the Pedlar lay down on the top of a large flat gravestone enclosed within a low iron railing. But hardly had he got his plaid tucked about him when a large ghost issued from underneath the stone and sat down on the iron railing.

" Are you aware that this is a murderer's grave? " inquired the Ghost.

" Is that so? " said the Pedlar, in a tone of annoy-ance. " Had I known that I would have gone else-where. I detest murderers—they are so restless."

" You needn't be so bitter," grumbled the Ghost. " There are murders and murders. Besides, the story is an old one now."

" Go on, then. But you must let me sleep after-wards."

" Right ! " said the Ghost. " Well, then, my father was a Cameron and was killed at Culloden. After that battle the Highlanders were a broken people, and began to scatter over the world. Many of them, strange to say, went into the very heart of their enemies' country —into London ; and what is more, they prospered there. I was one of those that went to London, and I pros-pered with the rest."

" Good man ! " exclaimed the Pedlar heartily.

" In London," the Ghost went on, " the English hated us like poison, and we returned the feeling. All the English wits passed their time sneering at us—the great Dr. Johnson among the rest. One night I met him in the street. ' Johnson, you fool,' I said, ' why are you always sneering at Scotland? Don't be making an ass of yourself—go to Scotland and then you will know what you are talking about.' He took my advice. But I digress. You may be sure we Scotsmen did not forget our native land. Clan societies were formed, and in the Clan Cameron I was a leading member. We hated the English so much that we never patronised their warehouses if there was a Scotsman in the same line. There were plenty of Scottish grocers, butchers, and drapers, but, strange to say, there was not a boot shop in London owned by a Scot. At last, however, a fine shop was opened, with the sign

Donald Cameron,

Boot and Shoe Maker,

painted above the door, and of course every Scot in London went there for his boots. The new merchant was doing a roaring trade. I called at his place several times to ask him to join the Clan society, but did not find him; and then one night, in consequence of a rumour which I heard, I walked straight into the back shop, where I found a villainous-looking Jew counting a pile of money. ' Ah ha! you scoundrel,' I shouted; ' you are the proprietor of this shop, and you have no right to the name of Cameron.' I said no more, but at once called a meeting of the Clan, and we cast lots as to who should settle the Jew. The

97

lot fell on me; and so, waiting my chance, I came on him in his shop after the staff had gone for the night. On the counter there was a large pair of tackety boots; I flung them at his head, and he fell, covered with wounds."

" Were you found out? " asked the Pedlar.

" Yes; and through the spite of the English I was brought to trial and sentenced to seven and sixpence or ten days. But the Prime Minister, Lord Bute, who was a good Scotsman, kindly came forward and paid the fine."

" Out of his own pocket? " asked the Pedlar incredulously.

" Not likely—out of the public funds," replied the Ghost. " ' You did well, Cameron,' his lordship said to me, ' but if you want to kill anyone else, for goodness' sake let it be an Englishman.' "

THE RIVALS.

WILLIE THE PEDLAR was once robbed of all his money, amounting to five shillings and ninepence, in a lodging-house, after which he always passed his nights in graveyards, where he could sleep in safety and without expense. Willie always avoided graveyards where any of his relatives or friends were buried, finding that their ghosts kept him awake asking questions and giving advice. He was therefore a good deal surprised to be wakened one night by the ghost of his grandfather.

" That you, Willie? " asked the Ghost. " Very glad to see you."

" I didn't remember you were buried here," said Willie, rubbing his eyes.

" What's fresh? " enquired the Ghost. " Father still living? "

" Dead! " answered the pedlar.

" I thought so," said the Ghost with a chuckle, as he sat down on a gravestone and laid his walking-stick beside him. " The folk nowadays have not the strength of their fathers—I was well over a hundred when I died."

" I know," said the Pedlar. " But I never heard why you are here. Why were you not buried in the churchyard with the rest of the family? "

" The fact is," replied the Ghost, " I did not want to be buried in the same place as Sandy Sutherland—he had a grudge against me. But it is a long story "

" All right—go on."

" Well," said the Ghost, " Sandy Sutherland and I were born the same year, and until we reached the age of a hundred we were the best of friends. We were then the oldest men in the village, and each of us got a purse of sovereigns. At the presentation I made a better speech than Sandy, and he never forgave me. Our chief quarrel, however, was about a young woman."

" A young woman ! " exclaimed the Pedlar, taking his pipe from his mouth and staring incredulously at the Ghost.

" Yes, a young woman," said the Ghost sharply. " Love never dies. However, she refused both of us— said we were too old."

" Strange—very strange ! " muttered the Pedlar.

" That did not heal the quarrel," went on the Ghost, " and at last the chief ambition of each was to outlive the other. Half the village had bets on me, and the other half backed Sandy. I was the stronger man, but Sandy was very dour—everyone said it was his dourness that was keeping him alive. I thought over this, and hit on a good idea. I went on a visit to Inverness, and a few days later I caused word to be sent home that I was dead. The news went through the whole village, and everyone believed it. When Sandy heard it he said—' Now I can die in peace ! ' A lot of his backers called to congratulate him, and they had a great spree."

" A great spree ! " repeated the Pedlar wistfully.

" In the morning," added the Ghost, with solemn joy, " Sandy was dead."

" A dirty trick ! " said the Pedlar emphatically.

100

"Yes, dirty—but well worth doing," argued the Ghost. "As soon as I heard that Sandy was dead I returned home and sent a message of sympathy to his family."

"Dirty—dirty!" said the Pedlar.

"Sandy's backers took a very serious view of the thing," the Ghost continued, "being angry of course at losing their money. They referred it to the village policeman, and he, who had backed Sandy, agreed with them it was clear case of murder."

"Murder—nonsense!" exclaimed the Pedlar.

"Of course," said the Ghost, "but all the same they could have made themselves nasty had I not diddled them."

"Diddled them—how?"

"Just diddled them," said the Ghost, with a hearty and triumphant laugh. "I died that night."

THE POACHER.

ONE night when resting in a Ross-shire cemetery Willie the Pedlar became aware that a Ghost was surreptitiously watching him from behind a tombstone.

" Come out of there! " said the Pedlar gruffly. " What are you staring at? "

The Ghost rose to his feet and approached in a shamefaced way. " I was chust pretending to myself that you wass a keeper," he said.

" You were a poacher, I suppose? "

" Yes, I wass that—and one of the best," the Ghost answered proudly. " But sport wass the death of me in the end."

" How was that? "

" Well," said the Ghost, " I met my death about a year ago in somewhat tragic circumstances, as they say in the papers—I wass drowned in the river."

" I have heard of you," said the Pedlar. " You were called Jock the Poacher."

" The same," replied the Ghost, with a gratified smile. " I wass known to every keeper within twenty miles, but best of all to the Laird himself."

" A greedy man, the Laird."

" Yes, as hard as nails; but one day I managed to get on the soft side of him. He had landed four big salmon, and I met him carrying them home himself. 'Ah, it iss yourself that iss the grand feesher, Laird—let me give you a hand to carry the feesh,' I said to him. So he gave me two of them to carry, and we began talking so friendly that it occurred to me to ask him for a day on the river; it would be a grand joke with the keepers—Jock the Poacher with a permit. So I praised the Laird's feesh so well that when we came to the castle he wass in fine humour. ' I have no change on me—come and have a trink of milk,' he said to me."

" Milk! " exclaimed the Pedlar. " That was shabby of him—very shabby."

" Shabby iss no name for it—I wass never more insulted in my life," answered the Ghost. " Well, I told him I would rather that he would let me have a cast on the water. He wass very stiff about it, but in the end I got the permit, and the next day I had great sport. That night I wass going to burn the permit when I noticed there wass no date on it— it wass good as long as I lived."

" He forgot to put in the date? "

" Yes; but how wass I to know that? " the Ghost asked cunningly. " So every cood feeshing day I wass on the river, and my son always came with a wheel-barrow to take home my feesh. Every time the Laird saw me he wass more mad than before; but he iss very proud of his forebears, and I had only to show the permit and say it wass a new thing for a Highland

103

chentleman to go back on his word. Well, on the opening day of the next season I wass feeshing the big salmon pool when the Laird came along the bank with a queer sort of smile on him. ' I see I must chust give in to you, Jock,' he said. ' Give me the permit so that I will fill it in in a proper way.' So I gave him the paper, and he wrote on it that I wass at liberty to feesh on his estate as long as I lived. Then when I wass putting it into my pocket he took advantage of me and pushed me into the water and drowned me.''

'' Served you right,'' said the Pedlar.

'' I don't deny that, but all the same I am having my revenge. What sort of man iss the Laird now? ''

'' They say that his mind is going.''

'' I quite believe it,'' said the Ghost, '' and the reason iss this—he hass not caught a feesh since the day of my death. Other men fill their baskets, while he never gets a bite. For when his fly touches the water a shadow falls along with it—a man's shadow that sends the feesh flying to cover. That shadow iss chust myself. I dog his footsteps—he will never catch another feesh.''

'' You say you can cast a shadow. I did not know that a ghost could do that,'' said the Pedlar.

'' That is all nonsense,'' replied the Ghost, testily. '' I am a ghost myself, and I know what a ghost can do. I tell you that since that day the Laird hass never caught a feesh.''

'' He is a keen fisher,'' said the Pedlar. '' It is a terrible revenge.''

'' Yes,'' said the Ghost, with a diabolical laugh. '' It iss far, far worse than death.''

PENSIONTOWN.

Rome, as Julius Ceasar profoundly remarked, was not built in a day; but against this you may put the almost instantaneous growth of Pensiontown. Not a stone of that populous and thriving town indeed was laid until long after the passing of the Old Age Pensions Act, and if you now take the trouble to visit the wilds of Aberdeenshire and see the town you will be surprised and gratified at what the old men of Scotland have been able to accomplish in so short a time. The population of course consists entirely of old-age pensioners, who find that, while in most places their pension would be barely sufficient to sustain life, the economic arrangements in Pensiontown are such that they can live there in comparative comfort. In their social and municipal life seniority is the great thing. Every man's rank or status is determined by his age, and hence it is that, while Mr. Alexander McCaskill, 123 years of age, holds the honourable position of Provost of the Town, Donald Grant, an urchin of 71, has meantime to discharge the lowly duties of scavenger.

When it became known in Pensiontown one evening that a prominent member of the Government was to pass the night at the inn in consequence of a motor breakdown, the Town Council at once decided to send a deputation to wait on him. The increased cost of tobacco and spirits had been pressing with great severity upon the aged community, and it was felt that an effort should now be made to have the town relieved from the payment of excise duty on these necessaries of life. The deputation consisted of:—

Councillor George Ross, funeral undertaker, aged 114.

Councillor Matthew Hossack, sculptor, 107.

Councillor Samuel Haddow, gravedigger, 106.

They found the Cabinet Minister sitting on an old-fashioned stool, drying himself before the kitchen fire. He explained to them that he was just about " fed up " with deputations, but agreed to hear what they had to say. George Ross, who was to put in a plea for duty-free snuff, passed round his mull; and the sculptor was going to call for refreshments, but the Cabinet Minister generously undertook that matter himself. " No, no," said the Cabinet Minister, " this is my shout."

Ross then explained that snuff was the very breath of his nostrils to him and to others in the town, and Hossack deponed that if he could not have his bit of tobacco he would sink into a premature grave. The gravedigger stated that he had heard their venerable Provost in the Council Chamber boldly attribute his longevity to his habit of taking a drop of spirits every night before going to bed, and this was heartily corroborated and concurred in by the other two centenarians.

" I shall require to think it over," said the Cabinet Minister, " but meantime we might have a game of dominoes. I have not heard the rattle of dominoes for weeks."

Draughts is the chief recreation for Pensiontown; but when the inhabitants feel in the mood for " going their mile " they play dominoes. The party had a great night of it, notwithstanding that the Cabinet Minister was temporarily indisposed by trying a fill of the grave-digger's " thick black."   Strange to say, the deputation entirely forgot that night to make further reference to the object of their visit.   It was not till next morning that they realised they had received no definite reply; and when they hastened to the inn they were just in time to see the Cabinet Minister's car disappearing over the Aberdeenshire hills in a cloud of dust.

THE EMIGRANT.

ONE day, fishing a mountain burn, I sat down on
the bank for a rest, and had just got comfortably settled
when I noticed there was a man sitting within a few
yards of me. His rod lay beside him, and there was
a look of deep dejection on his face.

" Not much doing to-day," I observed.

" I suppose not—I have not wet my line," he
answered indifferently. " But I remember in my boyhood the fishing here was very good."

" You are a native of this district, then? "

He drew near and looked at me earnestly. " I am
Lord Edderton—perhaps you have heard of me? " he
said. His tone was careless, but there was a strange,
hungry sort of look in his eyes.

" Lord Edderton! " I repeated doubtfully. " I
believe—that is—"

" No, no—don't perjure yourself," he said with a
gesture of despair. " You do not know the name—
is it not so? "

" I am afraid you are right."

" Well, did you ever hear of James Ross? " he inquired.

" James Ross—you mean the great philanthropist? Of course everyone has heard of him. Now that you mention it, he was made a Peer and took the title of Lord Edderton."

" You have guessed rightly—it was sheer guesswork. You forgot me just like everybody else," he said mournfully.

" No, no—everyone remembers James Ross anyway," I said.

" Perhaps so," he replied. " But when Lord Edderton is mentioned nobody ever can remember who he is."

" I fancy that might easily be remedied. If you continue to give a few thousands of pounds here and there and always make a point of putting ' James Ross ' in brackets after your name the public will soon get to know you under your new title."

" That is true," he admitted. " But as plain James Ross I had plenty of money to spare, while as a Peer I have a great style to keep up, and my contributions to public objects would necessarily be small compared with those I used to give. No man was ever more proud to get a title than I, but now I see I was a fool to have anything to do with it. As James Ross I was famous, while as Lord Edderton the public has lost track of me altogether."

" You should take this thing more philosophically," I remarked. " You yourself at least can never forget your identity, and you will always have the conscious-ness of having helped forward so many beneficent public schemes.''

'' It sounds all right,'' said Lord Edderton, shaking his head; '' but I am not cut out for a philosopher. I am a public-spirited man, and have a craving for recognition. Now, as I have said, I cannot afford to fling my money about as I used to do, because so long as I am a Peer I must support the rank with dignity. The only course left for me is to emigrate and drop the title altogether.''

'' Good gracious! Let me put it another way——''

'' No use arguing,'' said his Lordship, waving his hand impatiently. '' My mind is fully made up. I came here to-day not to fish but to think in the quietude of the glen. I now look on this stream—on these my native hills—it may be for the last time. In a new land and under a new name I shall make a fresh start in life. My fortune is ample to make an honoured place for me in the public life of the land to which I go. I sail from the Clyde on Saturday. Farewell, farewell.''

AN EXAMPLE.

WHEN young John Maclean went home to Skye after a long absence the first man he visited was his old friend, Rory Macdonald. Evidently Rory was on the look-out for him, for when John was about half a mile from the house the old man came out and began waving his hand joyfully. He then came down the cart track to meet his visitor, still waving his arm until he got within a hundred yards of him, when he began to bawl a hearty and prolonged salutation in Gaelic.

" Man, Rory," said John, " you are chust as young-looking as ever; there is no change in you at all. And yet," he added, with a puzzled look at the old man, " you do look a little different."

" Five years is sure to make a change," said Rory in a disappointed tone.

" No, no, it is not that. I know what it is now— you are not smoking. Where is your pipe? I hardly remember you ever being without your pipe in your mouth."

" Man," said Rory, " I am not caring now for the pipe as I used to do, and so I have given up the smoking altogether."

" Given up the smoking ! " repeated John in dismay, as he followed Rory into the house. " And me just looking forward to having many a smoke and crack with you, Rory—chust as we used to do."

" It began," said Rory, in a faltering voice, " with that little rascal my grandson taking my pipe away when I wass not looking, and making himself sick. He wass just daft for the pipe, although it made him so sick every time. So that made me think of stopping it."

" A good flogging——," growled John.

" On the top of that," continued Rory, " you know we have the new minister here, and he is terribly down on the smoking."

" He has no right," said John, warmly, " to come between a man and his pipe. Man, Rory I never thought you would knuckle down so easily."

" Well, you see," Rory answered, lowering his voice, confidentially, " I am getting to be a prominent man in the church now. Alastair Macinnes, the precentor, you know, has not been well this while back, and who but myself is taking his place."

" I have heard," said John, " that smoking is bad for the voice, but yourself has such a strong voice that it is not a pipe of tobacco that would spoil it."

Rory's vanity was touched, and he gave a satisfied smile. But soon he became grave again. " The minister's point," he said, knitting his brows, " is that

I have to be an example, seeing I am acting as precentor."

"Well, well," said John, "I don't agree with you at all, Rory. The best minister I know is a great smoker himself. But we will say no more about it. It is a pity, all the same, for I have here a roll of small black twist—the kind you used to like best. I brought it for you as a little present, but somebody else will have to get it, I suppose."

Rory reached out his hand and seized the tobacco, and his eyes went over it lovingly. "Ah, my tear poy," he said; "it is like you to be so kind to me. Thank you, Chonnie, lad—I do not know what to say to you."

"Why," exclaimed John, in surprise; "what are you going to do with it? What good is the stuff to you, seeing that you don't smoke?"

Rory's knife was already out, and he was hastily cutting a piece of tobacco from the roll.

"I do not smoke, Chonnie, my poy," he exclaimed, "but I chew."

H

THE SON OF THE SHEIK.

When Macgregor, the famous explorer, was in Arabia he became very friendly with Sheik Ilderim, and stayed for several weeks on the Sheik's oasis. During all that time Macgregor was never done praising Great Britain, his native land, his chief point being that it was the only free country in the world. The Sheik was greatly impressed by Macgregor's wonderful stories, and decided to send his son to Britain in order that his mind might be enlightened. And so when the explorer, mounted on a magnificent dromedary, left the oasis en route for Glasgow, the son of the Sheik was riding by his side.

Macgregor secured respectable apartments for his protégé in a quiet street near the University, where the young Arab was to take science classes, his great ambition, inspired by the big talk of Macgregor, being to irrigate the vast deserts of his native land. The lad was so apt a student that he might even have won a prize, but his reading was greatly hampered by the large number of street musicians who frequented the locality where he stayed. To him, after the quietude of the desert, the noises made by these men were intolerable.

The worst of these musicians was a man with a red beard, who played a cornet; and one evening the Arab went down and warned him that his visits must cease. A few days later, however, the man with the cornet was there again; he stood opposite the Arab's window, blowing defiantly and without pause save when he shook out the contents of his instrument and wiped his coarse red beard with the back of his hand. All around him the Arab heard windows being violently closed, and in a window across the street he observed a fellow-student shaking his fist at the cornet player. The son of the Sheik could bear no more. " This is a free country—Macgregor says so," he said to himself. He then loaded a revolver which Macgregor had given him, and shot the cornet player through the lungs. At first he intended to shoot him through the heart, but decided his lungs would be more appropriate.

It is strange how small a thing excites the people in these days. The son of the Sheik had barely time to close the window before a vast crowd had gathered round the dead body of the musician. Their faces were all bright with gladness, they pointed at the corpse, and shook hands with each other over and over again. The Arab was looking on in amazement when he heard a knock at his door, and the student from the other side of the street came hurriedly in and closed the door behind him. He then fell on the Arab's neck, and great sobs of joy convulsed his frame.

" If you had not done it, I would," he said. " But you must hide the pistol at once—the police might discover it."

" The police! " said the Arab, in consternation. " Surely they will not meddle with this—it was a purely personal quarrel."

" Nonsense! This is a hanging matter. You must deny all knowledge of the affair, and everyone is too grateful to inform against you."

If there was one thing in which the young Arab was specially proficient that thing was lying, having learned it from his father, who had become a Sheik by his greatness in the art. So when the police called they could make nothing of him. But he was disgusted with the fuss that had been made about the matter, and next day he set out on his homeward journey, carrying with him many presents from students, journalists, and long-haired poets who had seen him fire the shot.

On arriving at the oasis he found the Sheik sitting under an umbrageous palm, eating dates out of a pasteboard box with a glass lid on it.

" Welcome, my son! " said the Sheik. " You are early returned. What report have you of the land of Macgregor? "

" It is a land of wonders, my father, yet in it there is no freedom. They are enslaved by their own laws."

The Sheik combed his beard with his fingers.

" Strange! " he said, when he had heard the story. " I judged friend Macgregor to be a truthful man. But those explorers are all the same. There is none of them that speaketh the truth—no, not one."

THE APPRENTICE.

When the time came for Johnnie to leave school his parents decided that a commercial career was the thing for him, and so they got him a start in the great village emporium which belonged to " Duncan Macpherson, General Merchant." Old Macpherson at once began to let his new apprentice into the secrets of the business, cautioning him particularly respecting the fishwives, who were wont to drive very hard bargains.

" You see, Johnnie, mo laochan," said the old man, " when you are dealing with the feeshwives you must make them think that they are getting everything cheaper than everybody else, or you will never please them at all. Now, look you here at this yellow cotton —it is threepence the yard. But when a feeshwife will come for cotton you will show her this, and you will say to her : ' This is a very fine cotton, and the price of it is threepence half-penny the yard.' Of course she will then start to beat you down, and after a while you will chust let her have it at the threepence." Macpherson grimaced cunningly and took a pinch of snuff.

In a week or two the apprentice could deal with the fishwives almost as well as his master, and was pronounced by them " A nice, kind laad—none of your hard ones.'' But one day, in Macpherson's absence, a fisherman came into the shop, and for a moment the boy was puzzled. His master had not instructed him how to deal with the fishermen, whose shopping was almost invariably done by their women folk.

" I am wanting a pair of boots—Blucher boots,"
said the fisherman. He was a man of about seventy,
dressed in a well-darned blue jersey and baggy trousers
six inches too short. He had mild blue eyes and a
gentle voice.

" Yes," said the apprentice, smartly, and produced
a pair of " Bluchers," price seven shillings.

" What will be the price? " enquired the fisherman.

" Eight-and-sixpence," said Johnnie. " They are
a very fine boot."

The old man handled them thoughfully and gave a
suppressed sigh. " I will try them on," he said at
last. He would not hear of the boy removing his boots,
but Johnnie saw that they were very far through.

" They chust fit me splendid," said the fisherman.
" Eight shillings and sixpence," he said to himself,
" but they will be very cood boots—yes, I am sure
they will be extra cood."

" They are a very fine boot," the boy repeated in a
halting voice. He was now in terror lest the fisherman
should not ask for a reduction in the price.

" I will take them," said the fisherman, after a long
pause. He spread out the money on the counter—
two half-crowns and the rest in very small change. " I
think that iss right," he said, with a watery smile.

" Yes, it is right," Johnnie answered. His hands
were trembling so much that he had difficulty in tying
the string of the parcel.

" Then I will be going," said the fisherman. " Good-
morning to you, laad, and thank you."

The apprentice gazed stonily after him as he went

slowly down the street with his purchase under his arm. "A poor old man," said Johnnie to himself. "A poor, poor old man; and it is me that has cheated him. And maybe he has not another sixpence in his pocket." With a sob he gathered up the money and put it into the till.

THE SORNER.

Many were the tales told to Willie the Pedlar by the ghosts in the churchyards where from time to time he passed the night. One of these, which may be called "The Sorner" (one who takes food and lodging by force or threat), Willie regarded as among the most remarkable of his collection thus acquired.

The Pedlar was lying awake one autumn night in the ancient burial-ground of an Inverness-shire village when the Ghost of a smallish man drew near and addressed him timidly.

"Perhaps you do not know me, Willie, but I have known you by sight for many a year," said the Ghost.

"Who are you?" enquired the Pedlar gruffly.

"I am James Grant that used to live in the Big House up there in the wood, where my wife still lives," replied the Ghost.

The Pedlar raised himself on his elbow and looked at his visitor with interest.

"James Grant—the man that was known as Grant the Quaker," he said. "Yes, I mind you well. Not a bad fellow you was—and bought many a thing from me out of my pack."

The Ghost nodded. "You will, then, not object perhaps to listen to the story that I want to tell you," he said. "If I was kind to you, you should be kind to me, for it will be a relief to me to tell you the thing that lies on my mind."

"Well, well, go on then," said the Pedlar. "I could be doing with a draw of my pipe anyway."

" I suppose you know," said the Ghost, " that the Big House was left to my wife and myself by our master, Mr. Thomson the Quaker, on condition that we also became Quakers. His house and his fortune was left equally between my wife Catriona, who was his housekeeper, and myself that was his man of all work, and so we thought that the best thing we could do was to get married."

" Not very romantic—not a love affair," said the Pedlar.

" Not at first," replied the Ghost, " but afterwards —yes. Well, there was one important condition in the will that was not known to everyone, which was a lucky thing for my wife and me. Mr. Thomson willed that the house must always be open to give shelter and food and a share of everything we had to any Quakers who might come to us for help. If we failed in this we were to lose everything and the estate would go to the King."

" So that was how you became Quakers? " said the Pedlar.

" That was how," replied the Ghost. " In all my life I have never met a finer man than my master, Mr. Thomson; I have never met a man that was so fair-minded and generous; so you will not think it was a disgrace to us to follow his kind of religion."

" I would have done the same myself," replied the Pedlar. " Give me the chance and you will see."

" Well," went on the Ghost, " we lived for quite a long time without any Quakers coming to ask for a share of what we had, and we were doing well and saving money; but at last one night a man came to the house and said he had joined the Brotherhood and demanded assistance. Who do you think, Willie, was the man I speak of? "

" I have no idea," replied the Pedlar. " Your master and afterwards yourselves was the only Quakers I ever knew."

The Ghost was silent for a while and spoke at last in some agitation.

" The name of that man was James Forsyth—you knew him? "

" James Forsyth! " exclaimed the Pedlar in surprise. " Yes, I knew him, but I never knew he was a Quaker. As I knew him, he was a fellow without religion or even common decency."

" You do not know how true are your words, Willie," said the Ghost, with a sigh of relief. " I have said I have not known so fine a man as my master, and I now say that I did not think the world contained so dirty a rascal as Forsyth turned out to be."

The Pedlar sat up and regarded the Ghost intently. " What became of that man Forsyth? " he asked.

" Just wait," said the Ghost. " Forsyth, as maybe you know, was at one time a lawyer's clerk, and he was clerk to Mr. Duff, the lawyer that had my master's affairs in hand. He knew all about Mr. Thomson's will and the condition in it that we had to help any Quaker that would apply to us. So what did he do but turn Quaker himself."

" Him a Quaker! " said the Pedlar scornfully. " That man had no more religion than I have myself."

" I will take it on me to say he had less," replied the Ghost. " But he came to us and demanded a third part of Mr. Thomson's estate, threatening that if we refused he would bring crowds of others like himself who would profess to be Quakers and demand their share."

" But was there to be no test to show that they was genuine Quakers? " enquired the Pedlar.

" No test at all—how could there be? " said the Ghost. " He swore he was converted to be a Quaker, and what could we do? A man belongs to a religion if he professes it, and he professed to be a Quaker."

" It is funny I never heard he was one," said the Pedlar.

" I do not think," said the Ghost, " that Forsyth mentioned his conversion to anyone but my wife and myself. If he had done so he would have spoiled himself with people of other religious bodies. He was just a blackguard without principle or conscience."

" What became of him? " enquired the Pedlar again.

" Just wait," said the Ghost. " Not a week passed without him coming to our house and demanding money—as a rule he came when I was not there; and my wife as you can understand was kept in a state of terror. Before long he was getting not only a third of our income, but more than a third. Owing to his heavy drinking and disgraceful life, Mr. Duff, the lawyer, was compelled to give him the sack. We then became almost his only source of livelihood; and at last he did the only terrible thing that remained—he came to live with us in the house."

"You was a fool, James Grant, to let him over your doorstep," said the Pedlar, spitting contemptuously on a neighbouring tombstone.

"I was a small man—he was a big man—and he came," said the Ghost sadly.

"Could you not get a gun?" demanded the Pedlar.

"Wait, wait," said the Ghost. "Have patience, Willie. I saw all too well that Catriona was just about heart-broken with the trouble and disgrace of keeping house for such a fellow; and what was more I saw her look sometimes at myself with a kind of reproach, or even scorn, in her eyes. Then, Willie, I saw that, Quaker though I was, I had to do what I hope you will never have to do. There was only one thing that would shift that sorner from our house; and you know what that thing would be."

Willie nodded. "How did you manage it?" he asked.

"I managed it," replied the Ghost. "Our master, Mr. Thomson, was a great man for his garden, and had a knowledge, I think, of every plant that grows. I could not be his servant all those years without learning a good deal about herbs of every sort—among them those that are poisonous."

"Ah! so that was the way of it," exclaimed the Pedlar.

"That was the way of it," admitted the Ghost quietly, yet with a sort of triumph in his air. "I did not go to the chemist's shop and ask for a dose of poison—not likely. You can find deadly poisonous plants growing at almost any roadside, so I just made

124

up a dose of my best home-brewed stuff and put it in his whisky. No good putting it in his food, for he might not take it; but whisky he would never refuse. I sat up late with him that night drinking a good deal myself, and when my dear wife Catriona rose in the morning the house was clear of him for ever.''

'' How did you get rid of the body? '' enquired the Pedlar.

'' I thought it out well,'' answered the Ghost, '' and the hardest part of it was to take the fellow on my back and carry him to the river. When I got him there I tied cork floats to his head and feet before I shoved him in. There was a good moon, but the sky was cloudy. The river was not in flood, but there was a strong flow that would likely have carried him without the floats; but I did not take the risk. I launched him well into the water, and then took over the hill to the Ford to watch for him there.''

'' About three miles,'' said the Pedlar. '' How long did he take? ''

'' I can never forget the fright he gave me,'' replied the Ghost. '' What a fright—what a fright! ''

'' Did he not arrive? ''

'' Arrive!—he was there before me, and I had to rush into the water to catch him before he passed the shallows. However, I gripped him and drew him to the side where I cut the floats off him. I pushed him off on his journey again, and I suppose that from that day to this he has never been heard of.''

'' What explanation did you give your wife? '' asked the Pedlar.

" I never explained—I said I did not know where the scoundrel went," answered the Ghost. " But of course she knew I was out all that night, and next day her eyes followed me with a kind of fear in them."

" Did the thing not turn her against you? "

" Never," answered the Ghost, " although I am certain she knew I was guilty. It is more than likely I talked in my sleep. Now, Willie, what do you think of all this—can you blame me for doing what I did? "

" Blame you! I do not blame you," replied the Pedlar, heartily. " You had to look after your wife, and you rid the world of a low dirty scoundrel. If your wife did not condemn you——"

" She never did—never—never! " exclaimed the Ghost, clasping his hands. " Indeed I think from that night she grew more kind to me than ever before. I do not say that she loved me, but she knew that I loved her, and she was fond of me in spite of all. She is one among a thousand—among ten thousand. And you know, Willie, and all in this place know," continued the Ghost, in a loud voice, " that although there are no Quakers here, we have not kept our master's wealth, for with it my Catriona is tending the sick and feeding the hungry. As for me, guilty I am, but my Catriona, an angel, will plead for me before the Throne."

FATHER CHRISTMAS.

LONG ago there was a little orphan boy whose name was Mackay. His parents came from Sutherlandshire to the city where the man got a job as a carter. The foul air of the city did not agree with them, and they both died young. Their orphan boy made his living by selling newspapers and matches on the streets, and at night he slept among the hay in a stable. The owner of the stable knew that Mackay was an orphan, and was sorry for him, so he allowed him to sleep in the stable on condition that he never brought any matches there, in case he might set the hay on fire. There were rats in the stable, and Mackay at first was afraid of them; but they seemed to know that he was only a poor orphan, so they left him alone. The horse, too, got to like him so much that he could never go to sleep until he knew that Mackay was safe in bed.

One Christmas Eve Mackay was awakened by something falling on him, and saw a big man with a long white beard standing beside him with a lantern in his hand.

" I have seen pictures of you—you are Father Christmas," said Mackay.

" You are right," answered the big man. " I am sorry I awakened you. I put this mouth harmonium in your stocking, but you see there is a big hole in it, and the harmonium fell right through and struck you."

Mackay thanked Father Christmas joyfully, and began to play very softly on the mouth harmonium.

" You can play," said Father Christmas, patting Mackay's head. " But why not play louder? "

" Must not waken the horse," replied Mackay. " He is a big lorry horse, and works terribly hard all day. He is very strong."

" Good boy—good boy—you are right to think of the horse," said Father Christmas. " Now, what else do you want?—you see I have a lot of toys here."

Mackay looked at the toys and shook his head. " These are only for children, and I have no time to play with them anyway," he said gravely.

" But you are only a bairn yourself," said Father Christmas. " How old are you? "

" I don't know—nine or ten, I think," Mackay answered. " But I am kept very busy."

Father Christmas paused, and tears came into his eyes. " This is a hard time for children," he said sorrowfully. " When I was a little fellow like you I did no work at all. The Druids provided toys for all the children. But that is hundreds and hundreds of years ago."

Mackay stared hard at Father Christmas. " What is a Druid? " he asked.

" I was the Chief Druid," said Father Christmas, " and my business was to arrange sports for all the people in Scotland and provide toys for the children. We made groves in the forests to play hide-and-seek in, and in places where there were no trees we set up large stones and had rare games among them."

" And you were the Chief? " said Mackay respectfully.

" Yes," replied Father Christmas. " If you ever saw pictures of Druids you would notice that all of them had very long beards. My beard was the longest in Scotland, and so I was made Chief Druid. I now live in Fairyland, of course, and come here only once a year."

" Where is Fairyland? " asked Mackay.

" Far away among the hills," Father Christmas replied. " But now I must be off—I have a lot of calls to make on boys and girls to-night."

" You will come next Christmas? " said Mackay anxiously.

" You may be sure of that," Father Christmas answered. " So long as there is such a lot of nice boys and girls in Scotland I could never be happy without seeing them every year. Good-bye ! "

I

LORD ULLIN'S DAUGHTER.

Ever since the publication of Campbell's well-known ballad it has been popularly supposed that Lord Ullin's daughter and the Highland chief, her gallant and romantic lover, were drowned in Loch Gyle when endeavouring to escape from the vengeance of the wrathful Lord Ullin and his men. Far too many tears have already been shed over Campbell's garbled version of the tale, and the present writer has therefore set down the actual facts of the case in order to give them world-wide publicity.

The story opens on a stormy night in the month of October. Lord Ullin had gone to bed, and his lovely daughter—her name was Margaret-Ann—had retired to her room. Lord Ullin thought that she also had gone to rest, but in this he was deceived. For several hours she waited in the darkness of her room, and was beginning to fear that her Highland Chief, whose name was Roderick-Donald, was not going to turn up, when she heard the peculiar whistle by which he was wont to make his presence known. Her heart beating wildly, the girl approached the window; but suddenly she started back in alarm, for she beheld a pair of glittering eyes staring in at her from the outside. Her terror, however, was but momentary, for she recognised the countenance of her beloved Chief; she knew him also by the size and hairiness of the hands by which he was holding on to the window-sill.

" Margaret-Ann," said the Chief, in a hoarse whisper, thrusting his large red face nearer to the window, " Margaret-Ann, I am here."

" Dearest Roderick-Donald," said the girl passionately, " I see you."

" I am late—I wass detained," said the Chief. " There iss no time to lose. Are you ready for the road? "

Making no reply save a smile of infinite sweetness, the girl handed a small box, containing Lord Ullin's family jewels, down to the Chief, and then jumped lightly from the window to the ground, to be immediately enfolded in the protecting arms of her lover.

" Sweet Margaret-Ann," said the Chief with deep emotion, as he stowed the jewels into his capacious sporran, " it iss a brave deed that you have done this night. Yes, it iss very proud that I am of you."

The lovers then gazed for a while at the stars.

" They are very bright to-night—the stars," said the Chief in a sentimental voice. " And do you hear, my love, how the trees are groaning in the wind? "

At this moment the lovers heard the sound of a window being opened, and looking up, to their consternation they saw the head of Lord Ullin, clad in a red night-cap, protruding from his bedroom window.

" Who is there at this time of night? " demanded his lordship in an angry voice.

Margaret-Ann was terror-stricken. " We are discovered—let us fly," she whispered.

" It iss sorely against my nature, but I see nothing else for it," answered the Chief gloomily. So saying, he gave the maiden the assistance of his brawny arm, and together they began their long flight to the Isle of Ulva, where the Chief had his home.

For three weary days and nights the lovers struggled bravely on. Margaret-Ann's boots were almost worn away, while those of the Chief were rattling up and down his legs, the soles being entirely gone. Still, they made excellent speed, and it was not until the fourth night, on reaching the shore of stormy Loch Gyle, that their pursuers appeared in view.

"Margaret-Ann, my darling," cried the Chief, " we will have to take the boat, or perish. Here, boatman— a pound if you take us over the ferry! "

The boatman was asleep in his boat; at the mention of such a handsome remuneration, however, he sat up and began to rub his eyes.

"Hurry—hurry! " urged the Chief, as he saw the pursuers fast approaching.

"And who will you be? " demanded the boatman, eyeing the couple suspiciously.

The Chief began to hold forth at some length on his pedigree and family history, till he noticed the boatman was not listening. The mariner's eyes were fixed on the face of Margaret-Ann—he was entranced by her indescribable loveliness. He grasped her hand in his enormous paw, and kissed it fervently.

"I don't want your dirty money," he yelled. " I will do it for the lady's sake "; and thereupon took to his oars with goodwill.

As the lovers were launched forth upon the surging waves they could see on the shore the forms of warriors silhouetted against the sky; and they could hear the frightful language of Lord Ullin, ably assisted by his henchmen.

As the boat neared the centre of the loch, the men on the shore stood together watching; and it may be that into the hard and stony heart of Lord Ullin some paternal feeling was coming at last. Such had been the terrific force of the storm that the clouds had all been swept from the sky, which was clear and beautiful; while on the earth and sea there was nought but storm and fury.

Lord Ullin strained his vision after the receding boat. Suddenly he gave a cry of anguish; for he had seen the boat capsize in the middle of the loch.

" Come back! " he roared frantically. " Come back, Margaret-Ann, and I will forgive your Highland Chief."

For some time longer Lord Ullin watched for the re-appearance of the boat, but all, alas! in vain. So far as he knew (to quote the words of the able but un-reliable Campbell)—

" The waters wild
Went o'er his child."

And he was left lamenting.

II.

But we must now return to our hero and our dearly-beloved heroine. Lord Ullin's eyes had not deceived him when he saw the boat capsize. The accident happened as follows:—

Macpherson the boatman cultivated the dirty habit of chewing tobacco of a very strong and deadly brand,

and as he was far from being a particular man, he happened to squirt some tobacco juice upon the lady's dress. The Chief's jealous eye was quick to note the incident. " Fool," he cried angrily. " Do you think that the lady's dress wass chust meant for you to be spitting on? "

The boatman stared at Roderick-Donald in amazement, and slowly shifted his plug from one cheek to the other. He then took a marlingspike which he kept specially for such emergencies, and was about to hit the Chief a vigorous blow on the head with it, when Roderick-Donald, blazing with wrath at his presumption, drew his sword, lunged fiercely at the boatman, and thus upset the boat.

" Sweem clear! " roared Macpherson. " I will sort her in a minute."

And admirable indeed was the skill shown by the boatman on that stormy and eventful night. Long experience and constant practice had made him a master of the art of putting that particular boat to rights when she got upset, so frequently did that catastrophe occur.

The Chief could swim like a duck; but for a moment the fury of the waves was too much even for his strength. When at length he managed to look around him, a sight met his gaze which, notwithstanding the coldness of the water, made his blood boil. The boatman, holding on with one hand to the keel of the boat —his grizzly countenance dripping with water—was supporting Lord Ullin's daughter round the waist, and was in the act of imprinting a hearty kiss upon her lips. In that moment of delirious joy he seemed oblivious of the presence of the Chief; but a yell of un-speakable fury from that injured lover brought him to his senses. He started violently, and let the damsel go; and with a faint cry of despair she sank below the foam-crested billows.

But ah! in that dread hour her true Highland knight was near. Like a shot he dived to the bottom of the loch, and—after groping about for a while—found her and brought her to the surface.

By this time the boatman had got the boat to rights, and assisted the lovers to get in. Macpherson now exerted all his strength, and, after many buffetings of the storm, succeeded at last in bringing the boat and its moist and exhausted occupants to the shore.

The first thing the lovers did on their arrival was to marry each other, which they did across the sword of the Chief. The marriage feast, which took place in a crofter's sheiling, consisted of boiled potatoes and salt fish. The honest and heroic boatman was the only guest, from whom, however, the Chief parted in some displeasure, as Macpherson insisted upon having his silver pound for rowing the lovers across the loch, and laughed to scorn the Chief's well-grounded contention that he had offered to do the job for nothing.

III.

When the young couple arrived at the Chief's castle in Ulva, they found that a terrible thing had happened. The clansmen had heard that their Chief had married the daughter of their mortal enemy Lord Ullin, and such rage had seized them that they had deposed

Roderick-Donald and elected another man in his place. When Roderick-Donald heard the news, he killed eighteen men on the spot; but the clansmen were firm, and the deposed Chief had to take up his residence in a small one-room-and-kitchen house (bathroom and scullery, H. and C.).

"Darling Roderick-Donald," said the daughter of Lord Ullin a fortnight later, "what shall we do?—there is no meal in the house."

Roderick-Donald gave a ghastly and haggard smile. "Are there any potatoes?" he asked tragically. "Have we feenished the potatoes?"

"Not quite," said Margaret-Ann. "But hush! what is that?"

Someone was knocking at the cottage door, and presently an elderly man stepped into the room.

"My father!" cried Margaret-Ann, throwing herself into Lord Ullin's arms with such violence that two hens, which had been concealed under his cloak, fell to the floor.

"I was at the castle," said his lordship, "and heard of your plight. I managed to catch these fowls on my way here."

Tears of gratitude started to Roderick-Donald's eyes, and he wrung Lord Ullin's hand warmly.

"My people have rebelled against me," said Lord Ullin. "I came to you for assistance; but you seem to be as badly off as I am."

"It iss only too true," said Roderick-Donald gloomily. "After we have eaten the hens we will consider the situation."

Lord Ullin and his daughter divided one hen between them, and Roderick-Donald had the whole of the other one and the greater part of the potatoes.

After dinner, the deposed Chief produced his skian-dhu and picked his teeth with it. " This iss the only square meal I have had since we wass married," he remarked, " and now I am feeling equal to the night's work before me."

As he spoke he rose to his full height, which was 7 feet 9 inches, and proceeded to put on his best kilt and ornaments. He was indeed a magnificent specimen of a man; Lord Ullin began to be proud of him, while Margaret-Ann simply worshipped him.

" You will chust remain here," said Roderick-Donald to his wife and her father. " I go to regain my true position as the Chief of my Clan." So saying, he left the house and proceeded to the castle.

The new Chief was at home, and at that moment was surrounded by many of his retainers. He had been Chief only for a fortnight; but already there was keen disappointment among the clansmen that he had commenced no hostilities against any other clan or family. They felt that he ought to have signalised his election as Chief by a warlike expedition on a par-ticularly grand scale. Several of them were endeav-ouring to impress this upon him at the moment when Roderick-Donald, magnificently attired, entered the apartment. A whisper of admiration went through the crowd at his appearance. Never had he looked so well; he had eaten a hen and half-a-stone of potatoes, and this gave his bearing a new loftiness. His recent privations, too, had improved his looks; hunger had removed all suggestion of obesity, while prolonged thirst had given him a look of alertness and expectancy.

The first thing Roderick-Donald did was to go up to the new Chief and stab him to the heart with his skian-dhu. There was a murmur of surprise at the suddenness of the act; one clansman said it was really too bad, but Roderick-Donald took him by the beard and persuaded him to apologise.

" I am the Chief here," he roared in a terrible voice. " Get ready, every man of you, and follow me against our ancient enemy Lord Ullin."

There was a cry of approbation from the clansmen; this was the sort of thing they had been longing for.

" He hass insulted his daughter, who iss my wife," the Chief continued, " and I will teach him a lesson."

Next morning at daybreak the whole strength of the clan was on its way south to the territory of Lord Ullin, that nobleman himself—disguised in a kilt— accompanying the expedition. They found Lord Ullin's rebels totally unprepared for an attack; and Roderick-Donald fell upon them with his men, captured or killed every single one of them, and hanged the ringleaders on the spot.

Then Roderick-Donald addressed his own men and those of Lord Ullin. " Lord Ullin," he said, " will be restored to his castle and lands on condition that I—his son-in-law—am made his heir."

The majority of the clansmen were so much delighted with the success of the expedition that they were willing to do anything to please their Chief. A few dissenting clansmen, however, raised their voices, but these the Chief searched out and slew with his own hand.

" And now, chentlemen," said Roderick-Donald, " let us gather as much cattle as we can in this district —it would be a poor thing if we went home empty-handed."

This command was received with deafening applause. The old sennachie then insisted on making a speech. " Clansmen," he said, " Roderick-Donald iss the Chief for us. It iss true that he married the daughter of our old enemy; but oh! iss she not a lovely one? Fill your quaichs, chentlemen, and trink to the health of our noble Chief and his lady—the pride and the pridegroom."

THE SNAGGER.

WILLIE the Pedlar, whose name is now famous throughout the civilised world, once had a somewhat curious midnight interview with the ghost of a man who described himself as a snagger.

" What is a snagger? " the Pedlar enquired.

" Snagging," replied the Ghost, " is a very old and important industry. I was a snagger all my days, and my father before me. The chief part of the business has to be done at night; hence there are few people who know even of its existence. You know what a snag is, I suppose? "

" You mean the root of a tree in the bed of a river? "

" Exactly. Well, as you say you are an angler, I am sure you must have been struck with the large number of snags in the rivers you have fished—particularly the swift-flowing ones."

" Many a time," said the Pedlar emphatically.

" And frequently you have lost hooks and tackle in those snags? "

" That is why I stopped fishing," answered the Pedlar. " I lost so many lines that it became too expensive for me."

The Ghost chuckled. " It is a pity you did not know me," he said; " I could have given you lots of hooks and tackle."

" Thanks," said the Pedlar dryly. " But you have not explained what a snagger is."

" Well, you know already what a snagger is. A

snagger is a man who owns snags. I was the proprietor of several hundreds of them situated in the best Scottish rivers, and in the season I had scores of men in my employment."

" Good gracious ! " exclaimed the Pedlar.

" It is a fact," said the Ghost.

" But how did you come to own those snags—did you rent them from the lairds? "

The Ghost laughed. " Not likely," he remarked. " I have already said that the business of a snagger is done at night, and so he does not require to consult the landlord. I owned those snags because I placed them there."

" I am beginning to understand."

" You are a quick fellow," said the Ghost. " I went round my snags periodically, drew them out of the water, and detached all the hooks and tackle fixed in them. I then of course replaced them. On the whole I had a pretty difficult life of it, as many of my men did not treat me square—they used to take out the snags in my absence and sell tackle to anglers on the water. However, I made a very decent living out of the business—every year I got thousands of salmon casts and flies and sold them to the tackle merchants. In the off season I spent my time looking for suitable men and training them."

" What was their job? "

" Nothing simpler, but you would be surprised at the stupidity and backwardness of some of them. Their chief business was to wander along the rivers and decoy anglers to my snags. I myself did a lot of this. When

141

I saw an angler fishing for trout with the fly I would ask him did he not think of having a try for a salmon. I then would sell him a salmon cast or two and advise him to fish with bait and a heavy sinker, as if he did that his hooks were sure to fix in my snags, which of course were always placed in the finest streams and pools."

" A more cowardly and cold-blooded business I never heard of," said the Pedlar, staring with a scowl at the Ghost. " You are still a young man—how did you die? "

" I died at my post," replied the Ghost with dignity. " One dark night I was removing a heavy snag from the Spey. The river was in spate, and I had difficulty in keeping my feet. The snag came away suddenly, and the current got the hold of it and hurled it against me, knocking me off my feet. My head came against a sharp rock."

" And that was the end? "

The Ghost nodded sadly. " When I regained consciousness," he answered, " I was dead."

MACKAY'S LEGGINGS.

On leaving his father's farm in the Highlands to come to the city, where he had been persuaded to accept an important situation, Mackay took his leggings with him—a handsome new pair of yellow ones he had won at a ploughing match. One stormy day he observed that quite a number of men in the city possessed leggings and wore them in the streets; and that evening, in the privacy of his room, he stood on the table in his leggings to see how they looked in the mirror. To him it seemed there was something about them that was splendid and noble; and there and then, standing on the table, he determined that he too would wear his leggings at business. He put them on next morning. As he debouched from the close-mouth his face was pale and set; and strangers looking at him knew that here was a man it would be better to have as a friend than as an enemy.

In the warehouse the leggings were hailed with acclamation. All day men from other departments came streaming in to see them, and stood in groups near Mackay talking in loud whispers. "Have you seen them?" one man would ask another. "Seen what?" "Why, Mackay's leggings!" And then they would part, exploding with laughter. Mackay wondered how many times those shallow city fellows can laugh at the same joke. In the afternoon, just when he was thinking his trials were over, the manager came to him and asked him as a favour not to wear the leggings again. "They are a splendid article, but they keep the men off their work," said the manager. And so the warehouse saw the leggings no more.

But at night Mackay is his own master, and so he puts his leggings on and goes for long walks. There are crowds of people on his way, but Mackay does not see them; there is a strange power in his leggings that exalts his spirit and fills him with happy and noble dreams. He is no longer in the city; broad acres stretch before him; his eyes roam over a great farm, and his brain is engrossed with its problems. For Mackay is a farmer on a big scale, and the broad acres are all his own. He is taller, too, than most other men, and measures more round the chest; and he walks with long swinging strides and an air that is free and fearless.

Mackay's walking-stick is a heavy one, with knots on it. One night he discovered that by carrying it with the handle under his arm and the point slanting to the ground it felt exactly like a gun, and this discovery has added variety to his dreams. For when he carries his stick thus, with his finger crooked on one of the knots, his walk becomes slow and stealthy, and he is ready for any game or vermin that shows its head. Sometimes he lifts his legs very high, and goes with great caution; he is then among the turnips looking for partridges. One night a half-trained spaniel followed him for miles; but at last, discovering somehow that Mackay's gun was a fraud, it rushed homewards with yelps of rage and bitterness.

Leggings are not expensive, and are always worth the money. Although seldom prescribed by the medical profession, leggings are an excellent tonic. With a little imagination and a decent pair of leggings life in the city need have no terrors for the country lad, even though he seldom sees the face of a friend and his home and kindred are far away.

Printed by LAIDLAW & MACKENZIE, 95-97 Holm Street, Glasgow.